A Guide to
Natural
Meditation

If you want to get off the merry-go-round of medicine and therapy then this book is for you! If you are serious about improving and transforming your life and are prepared to do what it takes, Undo is the support you can draw on.

It has given me the missing link to rearranging my personal, business and financial lives to now be completely independent in ways I could never have imagined.

This stuff is REAL and CUTTING EDGE and you won't find anything else out there like it… I've been looking for 30 years.

—Peter Bergen, Lawyer
Western Australia

The approach taught in this book has real life solutions for my real life problems and I use it everyday. It changed my idea of meditation completely. I've used it as a tool for healing deep trauma and anxiety and the lasting effects have been immense. If you are looking for practical actionable solutions for healing that aren't based in religion or spirituality I'd say you have found the best resource available in this format currently available.

—Olivia Bryant, Chef
Australia

Extremely unique in its approach to meditation and how the body heals itself. The depth of the content and understanding is super impressive. It is very clear that the author of this approach actually knows what he's talking about. Thank you! Can't wait to really sink my teeth into this.

—Melissa Goodenough, Naturopath
Queensland, Australia

Natural meditation brought me back to life and showed me that we can heal and resolve anything that we've lived through, from the minor to the seemingly insurmountable.

—Helen Dubrovsky, Life Coach
Western Australia

This book gives you your power back because you realise that your experience of life is determined by your own internal beliefs, attitudes, preferences and so on, and as you get to the bottom of them and they dissolve, your whole life changes.

—Marcus LeClair, Entrepeneur
Chile

From using this approach here, I've resolved my fear of pain, which we are all encouraged to take on at a very early age. I now know pain is the body's language when you're too busy, distracted, resistant or egotistical to listen to the soft option! To have a fear of a perfectly natural healing process is a tragedy and only one of the things that this approach restores.

—Lee Trenton, Accountant
Canada

This author really gets to the fundamental realization that the body is where our true intelligence is, not our thinking. It demystifies the complexity of what we have been lead to believe, what the mind is. This understanding has changed my life, in so many ways for the simplicity and depth in appreciating what I am and I have no need to look for more. Thanks Undo! you are extremely needed in navigating the complex world we live in. It's revolutionary.

—Maryanne Shillong, Masseuse
Australia

… the more and more I go on, the more the simple and profound genius of this Undo process emerges. This is powerful stuff, and it is done well so that people can really tap into themselves.

—Zeus Yiamouyiannis, Ph.D. Author & Consultant
America

A Guide to
Natural
Meditation

Treating Physical and
Mental Health as One

MATTHEW ZOLTAN

Being Human Books

First printed in 2023 in the United States of America.
Typeset by Booknook.biz.
Printed by Amazon.
Cover Design by Erika Alyana Duran (easduran.myportfolio.com)

Identifiers:
ISBN 978-0-6457380-0-1 (Paperback)
ISBN 978-0-6457380-1-8 (Ebook)

CONTENTS

INTRODUCTION

IN 2016, MY WIFE AND I were in between businesses, taking a few years off to recharge and travel whilst looking for a new country in which to reside. We seemed to have outgrown Australia, changes in the community and people had been significant in the last 5 years. There was an unusual division and unease emerging that we didn't want to be a part of. So, we followed our insight and moved to Indonesia.

At the time, we were living in a 200 year old joglo in a small coastal village in Eastern Bali. My wife was relaxing reading magazines one afternoon, when she came across a small article in the wellness section about a popular meditation app called Headspace. She downloaded the app, did some research and some figures, then voiced her opinion. "If they can get over a million downloads with such shallow content, imagine what we could do to make a mark in the app industry. Let's create an app that's deep and profound. How would you like to put your work into an app?".

I took a look at the app and she was indeed right. The meditation they were globally promoting was, to me, a deterioration of what real meditation is. I have lived and breathed meditation since I was 18 years old and it is a very natural part of my life, so to me the app lacked authenticity and depth. I thought to myself, these guys are misleading people and trivialising something that has the power to heal and reconnect humanity. By using meditation as entertainment and a distraction from reality I could see how these practices would ultimately separate people from one another, rather than connect them.

I had been trying to figure out a way to get my life's work to reach and benefit more people and we were looking for a new direction in our business. This appeared to be an answer. I wanted to provide a truly clear and effective meditation approach that anyone could do. With the potential and opportunity to provide a real solution for the declining physical and mental state of humanity, I started writing the content for the Undo app. This book is a part of what came out of me during that time.

The purpose of this book is to introduce you to a new type of meditation that I coined Natural Meditation. I discovered the approach over 35 years ago. I'll go more into my history throughout the book but I'd like you to know that this unique approach has proven to be very effective and very powerful if you give yourself the time and space to take it in. This book is written in a way to resonate with and activate the wisdom already present within your body. This often leaves you feeling as though you already know what I am talking about, and you do know – well, your body does – but by me making it clear for you, you are able to realise that you do. Then you can become more actively conscious of that natural knowing present within you. From that point of knowing, you then need to know how to tap into it, what to do with the knowledge and how to benefit from it. I'm here to show you how.

As we all know, difficulties in life and the various influences we all face have an effect on our confidence and power. My aim is to show you how to get your power and confidence back, particularly when it comes to both your physical health and your mental health. The benefit of regaining the ability to be in charge of your health and wellbeing is that it frees you up from your fear around illness and pain. It also frees you up from having to visit the doctor so often.

I tend to use the word 'pain' to sum up and make it easier to communicate the entirety of all mental and physical afflictions, reactions and traumas. Freedom from the fear of all types of pain is one massive benefit of using my approach but it is the knock-on effects of that benefit that are even more immense.

Before you get started on the first chapter, as an exercise to try to comprehend how much time, money and energy you spend on trying to get rid of your pain, start to think about it in a different way. Some questions you might like to ask yourself would be how much effort do you put into trying to fix yourself? How much do you spend on trying to improve or change yourself? How much time, money and energy do you spend on avoiding your pain? How much time and money do you lose at work from being sick? What is the cost of that to your employer?

There are some pages at the back of the book for this exercise where you can list and tally up how much you think you would spend in a year or a month. There are three columns – money, energy and time. Consider reflecting on the areas where you might spend time and resources seeking comfort or escape. This could include various forms of entertainment, indulgences, or habits. Add them to the list and guess at how much you might spend on alcohol, recreational drugs, music, movies, porn, smoking, comfort eating, time spent on social media, buying things you don't need, gym memberships, watching sports, overanalysing your life, therapies, exhaustive searching, study, spiritual practices, etc. There may be others too, so list them and anything else that you know is harmful and that you know you use to escape the way you feel inside. Be really honest with yourself, you'll know how you avoid yourself and what things you do that cost you on many levels. Then, add them all to your list with a figure value that you can relate to.

How much time and energy do you spend excessively thinking or fantasising and daydreaming, and are these an attempt to avoid your real life? Now see if you can think past yourself and broaden yourself into considering the real cost that this has in your life and in the lives of others. Do you spend extra time standing in the shower vaguing out? What's the extra water and power cost of that? If you're in a bad mood in the morning, what does it cost your spouse, your children, anyone who gets in your way? And what does that stress then do to the rest of your busy day? Doesn't it just stress you out more? Doesn't it also add stress to anyone else in your vicinity?

While we're on the topic of avoiding your feelings, try to think about and consider what it costs your employer when you get to work and avoid the jobs that you need to do in preference for the ones that you want to do, just because they're easier. What does it cost your co-workers when you avoid your feelings and they eventually burst out of you onto them? What is the cost when you don't stand up in meetings and tell your co-workers what you know? What happens when you know that your colleagues are making a wrong decision and you don't say anything because you're afraid? What is that cost when you're too scared or feel too worthless or too whatever that feeling inside of you is telling you? You know that feeling that you avoid facing by not speaking up.

What is the cost to the company that you work for if your colleagues continue on the wrong course, just because insecurity, fear or another feeling prevented your own valuable contribution being expressed? What does that cost you, knowing that you didn't speak up when you knew what was right? What's the cost to you in how you are left feeling with that disturbance inside of you, whether you numb out to it or go back in and speak the truth?

Until that is resolved, you're not resolved. Numbing it out doesn't resolve it, it simply buries it deeper into your body. *Disturbance doesn't go away just because you think you can't feel it.* It only goes away if and when you feel it. And only then are you free to act the way you would without it.

It could take years to resolve the disturbance from that meeting, so then that disturbance has cost you a whole lot more than you ever realised it would. The cost to you is stress and energy depletion. Maybe I should design a hidden-stress cost calculator and then people might begin to understand what I mean when I try to explain the hidden costs of not feeling your pain. Not feeling your feelings, and then compounding those feelings over time, prevents you from doing what you should do and being what you really are, costing a lot more than you may realise.

Now, consider the cost of time – your time – and allocate your hourly rate to that. Calculate that out and tally it all up. You might be feeling a bit shocked by now.

Do you still think that distraction or whatever you do to avoid the way you feel really works to your advantage? Take some time and consider that. All that time, energy and money you put into feeding the feelings you don't like is gone, it's over, it's in the ether now. So, why not learn to be okay with the feelings that you think you don't like? At the very least it will cost you less in time, energy and money and the benefit is that you can let those feelings go, resolve them and move on. From here on, just try to be open to changing your ways, and not in the way that you have done in the past. If you find yourself still searching for answers or seeking a new perspective on meditation, then I ask you to be open to exploring my approach.

There will be so many more benefits than what I have just mentioned, and too many to list here, but another that you will be interested to know about is that you won't have anywhere near as much fear around being hurt in relationships or in life. You're going to learn the tricks and tools to pick yourself up and heal any adverse effects from life now, ongoing and into the future. You'll learn resilience and how to recover fast.

If one of the problems in your life is your health and it's costing you a fortune in more ways than just money, then this book can help you. When you're mentally unwell, productivity in any area of life, be it work, family or personal, declines enormously. When you can't focus your thoughts, you can't focus on anything for very long. If you're physically unwell or have chronic injuries or pain, it's the same; your thoughts are focussed on the pain in your body and not on your life. If you're not productive, you're not effective. If you're not working optimally then it's hard to feel satisfied or fulfilled and consequently, your life purpose and motivation declines.

But there is a way that will teach you to resolve your distress and continue recovering and improving your life daily so that you can truly live your life, not just survive it, and that is the Undo approach. It's not the easy road, it's not a quick fix, and you'll find it's not what anyone else is saying. It's what I have learnt and experienced and successfully implemented working with thousands of other people. What I am saying and in fact what you're about to find out is the polar opposite of what the majority are saying. But I know it works and I know it's achievable if you simply do what is written in the pages of this book.

It would be impossible to put everything I know into this small book but what is here will give you a comprehensive introduction. It will fast track you to getting started on understanding your pain, and you won't have to figure out all the mistakes I had to along the way. This is a lifestyle, a true change for the better and most certainly one for good and it's entirely up to you, well, your body, really. So, take it at a pace that you can handle.

By taking care of your mental health you are also automatically taking care of your finances, productivity, relationships and many other areas of your life. Virtually everyone I have worked with rarely visits a doctor or therapist. They rarely take pharmaceuticals and pain blockers unless they have an extreme physical injury. They heal everything naturally, and just through feeling and taking an interest in themselves and their pain. This takes the pressure off financially but also in many other ways too. By giving yourself the space and time to listen to your body's signals and learn its language, you can allow your body to do what it does best, and ultimately all it wants to do, and that is to keep itself in optimal condition and – HEAL.

Additional supplements or healing foods can give your body the correct nutrients to support and facilitate the healing, but what you think and what your body does all by itself to heal is more important and unfathomably more powerful than anything external to you.

By learning how to look after your mental and physical health you can save a great deal on medical costs and therapy. Just look at the total figures on your hidden-stress cost calculation. By reading this book, you'll learn that healing and recovering from the daily stresses of life and the past are possible through simply feeling your feelings and not avoiding them.

You need to understand what pain and illness are for and where they come from. That's where my expertise and approach can help you. That's what you'll learn from Undo. You need to know and understand that it is ok and normal to have pain and illness and that it shouldn't be rejected or fixed, which is how most other health modalities approach it. Pain and illness need to be understood. That type of understanding is an investment in yourself and in those who you affect, and it's easy to apply once you have the right guidance.

I'd like to explain the reason why we called the app 'Undo'. It is because most of my work is done by negating what you have already learnt or been conditioned to think. So, in that way, by learning this new approach to yourself you'll be unlearning, undoing many of your old ideas, beliefs, behaviours and harmful thought patterns. You'll learn how to undo at the root of all the tensions and pains, memories and traumas in your body. You'll learn to undo all the harm that you've picked up through just existing in this world.

There are a few things that you need to know as you read through the book. When I refer to Undo, I am referring to the app or the approach to Natural Meditation that I discovered.

This book is a small taste of the 500+ pages that I wrote for the Undo app, it's a companion book to it. You can read along whilst listening to the audio in the app, you just need to play the 'Primers' in each core chapter. A few words have been changed here and there but mostly it's exactly the same. The chapter numbers in this book match the ones in the app so you can easily keep track. You can follow along with or without the app, either way it's a thorough introduction to Natural Meditation and to navigating every area of your life.

There is a promotional code in the 'About' section at the back of the book to redeem my gift to you for buying this book and the app.

This is an interactive book. Wherever there is <u>underlined text</u> this means there is a corresponding section in the app where you can go to deepen your learnings. At the beginning and end of each chapter I ask you some questions that will help you to check in with yourself and consider what you have learnt. They invite you to ponder what has changed inside of yourself by reading this information. There is empty space for taking notes as well.

I hope you will want to use this book as a well-read go to guide on *you*, so bend it, tag it, write all over it, dog-ear it and keep it close. It will have your deepest understandings in it, but the best part is, it's all about you and from the most unplumbed depths of you. Getting to know yourself is one of the most interesting, surprising, entertaining and fulfilling things that you can do, you are a work in progress. Now let's get started.

CHAPTER ZERO
WELCOME TO UNDO

OVER THE LAST 35 YEARS of working my clinics and from running hundreds of silent meditation retreats, I have helped more than 30,000 people, just like yourself, discover the natural meditation of the body and re-activate the healing power of nature within themselves.

During this time of pioneering the Undo knowledge, I repeatedly found crucial areas of understanding that were missing from people's lives. From applying my learnings, my clients developed skills for a successful life and healed all manner of illnesses, both physically and mentally. It's this missing understanding that I'm sharing with you.

My approach isn't conventional, but it works immediately and is immensely effective. With uncommon sense and insight, I turn most theories and practices on their head. Everything that is said here in the Undo app, and in all my work, revolves around the themes of doing no harm, understanding the nature of your thinking, and learning to feel again by anchoring yourself in your body and senses.

I don't jump between different techniques or theories here. I focus solely on the discoveries I have made throughout my life that have had a major beneficial impact in my own life and in other people's lives.

The Undo app was created as a response to the deteriorating quality of meditation in the market today. From my late teens, I devoted seven years in meditation as a yogi monk and additionally, I have cumulatively spent more than five years—that's 24/7—meditating in the quiet retreats I lead. This gave me a vast and clear appreciation of what meditation really is. I wanted to share my unique approach in an app so that many would have access to the understanding that I have, and that is truly needed.

Undo was built to assist anyone who is yet to try meditation or who has been misguided or misled by traditional meditation, so that they can learn a more transformative, easier and deeper way to meditate, one without thinking ever being a concern. So it doesn't matter if you are a beginner or a seasoned meditator, this approach is for anyone.

Today's meditation has been westernised and the real value it can provide has been diluted, modified and morphed into entertainment. These approaches can help guide your thoughts, but they won't improve the quality of your thoughts. And that's fine if that's what you're looking for but that's not what Undo is about.

We're about waking you up, not putting you to sleep. We'll inspire critical thought and explain the complexity of the mind using straight forward language that resonates with you and makes complete sense. We'll show you how to integrate through the process of healing your pain or trauma. You'll discover parts of yourself that you have never known before, and you'll probably even find out that you enjoy being yourself—exactly as you are.

WHAT IS UNDO

Historically, meditation was used as a way to remove ignorance, enabling you to see yourself and the world as it is, and to acquire self-knowledge and oneness with yourself, that is, enlightenment. But as the majority of meditations out there today are technique-based, and because techniques for meditation are not about you or from you—they are an outside in approach—they won't resolve the effects of life or awaken you. Learned from the outside of you and from others, they simply add another layer of conditioning *to you*.

Undo is about deep, natural meditation. Natural meditation has nothing to do with a mind, soul or spirit. It's entirely about the living, breathing, feeling and thinking body of you. Reconnecting you with your current and natural state, it's only about you. This inside out approach arises entirely from within you, which is why it leads to insightful understanding all about you. It's the meditation your body does naturally to release tensions and heal the effects of life and it's how you evolve. When you apply it, you'll experience the life you already have to the maximum and so be completely fulfilled.

And as you progress through the Undo process, you'll learn to approach your health in a completely new, self-reliant and sustainable way. Rather than seeing mental and physical health as separate, you'll come to understand them as different expressions of the same distress that originates from deep within your body. You'll learn to activate your body's own healing forces at will and allow your body, which *is* nature, to heal at the source.

Undo is not a philosophy. Its knowledge is not mine. It belongs to everyone, because it's simply the recognition of the purely physical facts of nature and how we, as humans, work.

WHAT IT WILL DO FOR YOU

Undo works on the experiential level, giving you deep self-understanding. It is on the experiential level that you *know* in and from yourself, this is the level from where we all know when we are hungry, cold or tired and so on. At this level of physical sensation, you are in your depths, and this is where healing and recovery takes place.

Contrary to what you have been taught or even experienced, inside you there is an inbuilt solution to maintaining your optimal condition. By using the Undo approach, you'll re-activate this power within you to enable your system to better heal itself, and thereby establish independence in managing your state of health.

Step by step, theme by theme, the Undo process will awaken and build on your understanding of your whole self and how you work. You'll come to appreciate your body's wisdom—wisdom that naturally keeps you informed of all you need to know about you moment to moment and awakens and navigates you through life as you live it.

So, if you are currently living with trauma, chronic pain or mental illness, if you want to heal unresolved effects from your life experiences, or if you just want a meditation that actually works, then you've found the right place. The Undo process is entirely unique to you, fulfilling your deepest needs for recovery and reconnection with the whole of yourself, however that is.

WHERE TO BEGIN

We've intentionally designed Undo with as few distractions as possible. This gives you the opportunity for many quiet spaces during meditation, allowing you to experience whatever shows itself from within you. This meditation develops exponentially, allowing you to unlock what it is to be you.

Undo isn't about skimming over wellness tips or swiping at pictures. Understanding yourself deeply needs a commitment to push through the process. Before you begin reading the content, notice how you feel deep in your body, and explore this again during and after taking in this information to notice any change.

There are two areas of learning in the app, the Core Chapters and the Body Tension Translator. Each Core Chapter provides two kinds of meditation, along with the information and insight you need to meditate for long periods and with depth. In the Body tab you'll find the Body Tension Translator or 'The BTT' as we call it, and here you'll learn the correlation between a body part and the topic of your thinking, plus the deeper feelings that affect the health of that body part. This tool is clarifying and designed to connect you with your body.

The Core Chapters have been written to build one upon the next, so we encourage you to complete them in sequence. Each one addresses a key common reason why you have trouble coping with the various difficulties you face. This is the essential education on how to fully live your life, and how you can solve your own problems along the way, that until now has been unavailable.

This is not the type of information to learn swiftly and then apply. You'll miss its deeper meaning if you skim over it too quickly. The content is timeless. If you take it in slowly, it will take you deeper into understanding you, uncovering an amazing part of you yet unknown to you.

Regardless of what you have done until now, regardless of religion or culture, the Undo approach is about that which is common to us all. It's all about the body and how the body solves the problems of health and life in a way that is different to how thinking, sciences or ideologies can or have.

Undo simply reveals how to align with the natural workings of the body. When we learn how to listen to and be guided by them, everything takes care of itself naturally, and we recover from any unresolved imbalances, effortlessly. This type of change is perpetual and permanent. It's preventative mental and physical healthcare at its core.

The natural meditation of the body reintegrates your body and mind, connecting you and returning you to a whole and healthy state of being. Then you can live as you naturally and truly are, and be satisfied with being you.

Now it's time to go to Chapter one where you'll learn all about reconnecting. There, you'll learn how to reconnect to yourself so that you can be firmly grounded and anchored in the reality of the sense of yourself. This will be of great benefit to you in living with the distresses of life within yourself and your surroundings and get you started in this new approach. Welcome to a new era of your life.

Go to the Active Meditation for this chapter in the Undo app.

CHAPTER ONE
RECONNECT

IN THIS CHAPTER WE'LL BEGIN to stimulate your awareness by introducing a few primary themes to prepare you for the journey to come. Then together, we'll build a more comprehensive experience as you progress through all the Chapters. This will bring a new clarity into all aspects of your life as you fully flourish from the Undo approach.

FROM DISCONNECTION TO RECONNECTION

Undo's natural meditation is probably a complete reversal of what you think meditation should be. It's not about the mind, it's about the body.

It's not a way to change or improve yourself but the way to truly discover and appreciate yourself as you already are. To enhance the unique individual you are. And to discover your body's natural meditation for yourself.

It's not about disconnecting or detaching from the world either. Our aim is to show you how to resolve any disconnection between how you really are and how ideas or beliefs say you should be.

Ultimately, reconnection comes with realising yourself as one whole living organism, a self-governing sensitive body that feels, remembers, knows and thinks. Each of us are part of the natural world. When we are undivided by culture or belief systems of being superior to nature, we then discover the meaning of 'one'.

This is a discovery of the greatest consequence because from here you'll find that you are perfectly fine as you are, you just haven't appreciated or seen that yet. And it's only your learned biases about yourself that are blinding you to seeing that.

By going deeper than thought-based techniques and learned false ideas about yourself into the sensations of you in the feeling body, you will discover the truth of this for yourself.

This natural meditation is made up of and defined by all it is to be you. Undo will teach you how to purely feel again, and that by only feeling and not by thinking, you will discover that beneath all those ideas, you are perfectly fine, however you are.

UNDERSTANDING THERE ARE NO MYSTERIES IN LIFE

Mysteries are man's invention to confuse others into thinking there is more to life than there really is. So all I'll be doing here is revealing to you your own natural and already complete state. Reconnecting you with the life of you, the state of you that is natural and unique to you. It is, quite simply, already there in you and as you to be discovered.

Your problem, misery or dissatisfaction with yourself isn't the result of what or how you are. It's the result of how you have been taught to think about yourself. These learned thoughts are a type of brainwashing or social conditioning—a manipulation of your thinking, which forms your thought-reactions to yourself. These reactions take the form of judgements, criticisms and comparisons with imagined better ways to be through false beliefs about yourself.

You have been taught to dislike things about yourself and how you naturally feel inside before you ever had a chance to truly know yourself. How can you really know you dislike yourself when you don't even know yourself? You can't.

And as you can't, then there must be another view, a truer understanding of you that will enable you to really appreciate and be fulfilled with yourself as you are. And there is.

It is my intention to reveal to you a deeper sense of yourself that will allow you to see yourself in a very different light. A deeper, very different you than the one society has imposed or influences you to see and believe as you.

I'll also share my valuable insights into how healing in the body actually works. You'll discover how we carry the effects of trauma in our body from childhood through to present day. And how these effects actually change the way it feels to be you, and unconsciously affect your decisions and drive your destructive behaviours.

By reconnecting, you'll also learn how to sense and diagnose your own condition and support your own recovery from mental or physical health issues, allowing a process that is essential for the body to heal itself and remain well.

THINKING VS. SENSING

Thinking is only for dealing with the mechanical issues of life. The modern human tries to use thinking for understanding personal issues as well as mechanical ones and so has become more confused than ever. But when your response to life is based in your own ongoing sense of the greater facts of life, it becomes very clear and simple to relate to and understand.

That being said, even though you may have overlooked and taken this for granted, if you think about it, you will realise you can and actually do know in yourself that your experience and understanding of yourself and everything around you is primarily reliant on your senses; of seeing, hearing, tasting, smelling and touching.

At some level deeper within you, you also experience the way that all that sensory information entering your system stimulates your internal sense of life, which is actually known to you and is felt deeper within the body of you.

You know you have this deeper understanding, which is not just your thoughts about life and the world, it is your own real sense of everything you absolutely know to be true about yourself and the world around you.

For example: for a moment, think of someone you know well. Now, feel your sense of that person. This is your body's felt-sense of knowing all about them. In that one sensation or bodily feeling, notice how all the information you have about them is available to you in an instant.

Now consider putting all that felt *sense of knowing* them into thoughts or words. How long would it take your thoughts to know what you the body knows as a feeling in an instant?

You could write a book from your thoughts about this person but in an instant you have your full sense of them.

In comparison to physical sensation, can you see how your thinking is no match for the vast intelligence of purely sensing?

Your senses are also your body's answer to being deeply connected and fulfilled. Only through sensing do you truly connect with and know anything untainted and as it is, for sensing occurs well before any other influence becomes involved. From sensing, you will find all you need to know to solve and navigate life's obstacles as you live it, from and for yourself.

QUESTIONING YOUR IDEAS

Since birth, you have been told what to do, what to think, what to believe, what's good, what's bad, what's true and what's false, and so on. Most of the ideas you have learned and believed since childhood are not actually your own, and they prevent you discovering what is true for you. Unknown to you, they have given you a false perception of yourself and the world around you.

If the Undo content triggers any reactions, this will be a reaction from these hidden ideas you harbour. Many of these ideas have the effect of putting you at odds with yourself as you are. But because they have also been a part of your identity and a form of security for you for so long, it is these false additions to you that will feel challenged.

Try not to confuse feeling challenged with feeling judged. These are just your underlying and learned judgments of your own character also being triggered and revealed. Try to view them as opportunities to go deeper into yourself. By just feeling any disturbance in your body as it arises, you are already helping them to process and are helping yourself at the origin of your disturbance.

For example, any traditionally learned ideas on life, on how you should act or behave, or any ideas about meditation or health, will probably be challenged here. If you feel defensive or judged, this indicates that you are under influence without you even realising.

Our purpose is to expose these influences to you, and we're not going to replace them with others. This will allow you to differentiate your own thoughts from those of others and then show you how to re-discover everything from yourself.

OPENING UP YOUR NATURAL INTELLIGENCE

Undo isn't just an improvement on other meditations. It's a quantum leap into something else entirely. It's an education on life that awakens your deeper sense of yourself in the body, where your quiet natural intelligence lies. It's this quiet natural intelligence that you need to navigate and guide you through life.

This deeper sense of yourself and your natural intelligence comes together as the foundation of this natural meditation, making techniques to meditate antiquated and obsolete.

Traditional meditations and techniques are comprised entirely of thinking, so they actually *make* thinking a problem when you are meditating. Using them, you get stuck in the shallow repetition of the technique, which is more thinking, and you keep trying but failing to get any real and lasting depth.

It is essential for you to understand that thinking cannot penetrate into the depths of feeling. The thoughts or words 'sad' or 'fulfilled' or 'hungry' are only descriptions and are not the feelings they describe. Which is why techniques to meditate can never take you into the depths of meditation—that depth only exists deeper than thinking or techniques can go.

The Undo approach of natural meditation is uniquely effective because it bypasses thinking and takes you into the depths of yourself existing beneath thinking. It is here, in the deeper felt sense of your physical body, that you reconnect with how you actually are. In here, all thinking ceases to be a problem. In here is where you come to understand yourself whilst also contacting and healing any harmful effects of life that are held within your body. And as you heal, you will awaken and increase your access to your body's natural intelligence.

FINDING THE SOURCE OF ALL DISTURBANCES

The varied problems and distress that we are all faced with in life can seem complex and overwhelming. To simplify that complexity and relieve the effects on us the solution itself must be simple.

From birth to adulthood, a mass of education and ideas are imposed on us that tie us into severely limited perceptions of ourselves and the world. Belief systems of cultures, dogma or spirituality, formalised education and psychology all offer their ideals which essentially conflict with how and what we are. They offer the idea that as both a 'mind or soul' and a 'body' there are two of you, not just one. We are taught to think as though we are more than one thing or person, and then live in terrible confusion of who or what we really are.

During my time as a monk, my first extreme experiences of consciously living with this division between mind and body occurred. Throughout the day I'd condition myself with the various mental practices and disciplines of the dogma. But after about four years of this, at night, severe physical contortions began to occur during my sleep, holding me in a state between sleep and wakefulness.

As this was happening, I was still acutely conscious of my physicality, and throughout my body I could feel something within me was physically trying to break free. Something had begun changing on its own and it was a process I had no control over. This change was causing me to see the practices and ideologies I was applying in a different way and for what they really were.

The nightly contortions went on for about two years, during which time I presented many challenging debates with the organisation's hierarchy about the hypocrisy and shortfalls of our ideologies. Unsurprisingly, these weren't well received and by that time I was clear-eyed and unable to continue with the mental practices and dogmas. So, my monastic life came to an end.

In hindsight, I understood that due to the extreme self-control that I exercised, during my waking hours as a monk, it was only when I slept at night that my organic cellular intelligence could begin its process of breaking free of the thought-conditioning (belief system) I was imposing on myself during the day.

Eventually it occurred to me that the apparent existence of a *mind* or *soul* was entirely dependent on thought and imagination, and without that thinking, it simply does not exist. The entire foundation of my life as a monk, and any life I had constructed around a belief or a persona, was exposed to be entirely without substance, and so *'the monk'* died within me.

The idea of there being two or more of you destroys your foundational sense of yourself, which confuses and desensitises you to the self-evident fact that there is only one of you—the body. This false idea disconnects you from the natural physical alerts of distress, and numbs you to this source of sensed understanding within your body. And it's this primary source of sensed understanding that is required for sensing and then solving life's problems as you live it.

To resolve life's problems, you first need to understand that the mental or thinking part of a problem is just the shallow surface of it, and therefore not the point at which you will resolve it.

Then secondly, you need to know that the *distress you feel* as physical feelings in the body is the actual root of the disturbance. If you address the problem at its roots, at this common source of all distress, and feel it where it is in the body, the mental or thinking part, which we all suffer, will resolve itself and dissipate, every time.

We will explore this aspect in much more depth as you progress through Undo.

This simple yet essential ability to truly feel is lacking to varying degrees in nearly everyone. Furthermore, dogma, ideology, science, psychology, medicine and traditional meditation have completely missed the significance of this crucial and simple self-repairing function of our body.

There is an effective way—essential for us all—to recognise and resolve the various problems we are faced with at their origin. The *root distress* driving any physical or mental problem is actually held in the living flesh of the body. It is only by feeling it there, in the sensations of the body, that we are able to dissolve and end our distress or pain.

FEELING DISTURBANCE

Knowing how to truly feel is the essential key to undoing the effects of the problems you are faced with in life. Without this solution, your thinking remains reactionary, stressful and ineffective, and continues to tie you up in knots.

In order to resolve confusion, you must be free of the primary cause of confusion—which is other people's thoughts that you have mistakenly believed to be your own. You also need to feel and stay in contact with the pain or trauma from life that is held in your body, which is the opposite to what we are all taught.

By truly feeling your deeper disturbances, without judgment of how you should feel or be, disturbances within your body will resolve and enable the mental confusion and harmful behaviours they drive to come to an end.

In the process Undo takes you through, you will feel discomforts that you have been avoiding, which at first may be very disturbing. But as you learn to feel them without mentally reacting to them, you will discover that the feelings settle down and ultimately lessen and dissolve. Your life becomes smoother and easier. What seemed very challenging before becomes simple and straightforward. In this way the problems that could otherwise plague you in life become an acceptable and naturally resolvable part of life.

As you progress through the information here, you will find out what it is like to truly be yourself without judgment or learned self-views. You will firstly discover how in so many ways you are not yourself, and consequently, why you feel unfulfilled. You'll see how the thoughts you think are not really yours, and the life you think you desire is not what *you* really want, but is what you have been taught to want.

Do you know why you think what you think and do what you do? Are you not, in many ways, unknown to yourself? Influenced to such an extent, haven't you, in a sense, ceased to be you? Not being yourself or trying to be what you *are not*, is your only real problem. This you will find, is the basis of your unfulfilment with yourself as you are, and that all other problems that propagate in your life stem from this.

Understanding and applying this is your first step in healing what you perceive to be the worst in you, so that you can bring forward what is naturally you and so is the best in you. And through doing this, you will be completely fulfilled by what you are. Let me show you a new way, a different way.

We'll now move on to Chapter two where you'll learn all about Reactions and how you can begin being at ease with the fluctuations of your life. It will provide you with the understanding to help you recognise and resolve whatever causes you to react and resist the beneficial but often frightening challenges in your life. With this insight, you'll be able to dynamically and more rapidly move forward in life.

There is no rush and it is okay if you struggle to understand me at times. Any struggle indicates that you are pushing through the boundaries of your current limitations. You are struggling more against the effects of your learned and limited ways of thinking, rather than struggling to understand the content itself. The potential effect of the struggle is to prevent you from understanding anything unfamiliar or new. And as you struggle against these effects, it will help you to know that they may cause you to feel frustrated, challenged, or even stupid and want to give up or reject the challenge of new perceptions. This is normal and nothing to be worried about. Just keep going, and in time you will resolve and be free of these limitations.

You might complete most chapters the first time without fully understanding their depths and significance. And again, this is quite normal, because I am deliberately pushing you into new and unfamiliar ways of thinking and further into the depths of yourself, deeper than you have ever been pushed before.

When considering things unfamiliar to you, at first you can only know how it makes you feel. Then each time you reread a Chapter, the feeling of it within you will grow into greater comprehension. In this way, you will expand beyond your current limits and increase your intelligence and capacity for life from the inside out.

So be patient with yourself, the content and the process. Give it a chance to sink into you and ignite something new within you, and it will.

Go to the Active Meditation for this chapter in the Undo app.

CHAPTER TWO
REACTIONS

REACTIONS ARE MADE UP of beliefs, biases and unresolved painful experiences. All of these make it harder for you to respond sensitively, intelligently or rationally in day-to-day life. Understanding the mechanics of reaction is the foundation to navigating and resolving all disturbances in your life. From understanding reaction, you will learn how to easily end conflict and distress, which will help you thrive in all your relationships.

CHECK IN WITH YOURSELF

What annoys you about yourself or others?

What do you struggle with the most in your day-to-day life?

Do you find it difficult to cope with distressing situations or people?

Note your answers and then put them aside whilst you complete this chapter. At the end there will be a review of these questions to highlight your progress and help you realise the changes that have naturally happened within you in this process.

DISCOVERING YOURSELF IN DAILY LIFE

Typically, on the days we feel good, life around us *seems* better and we are generally less likely to be disturbed by the world around us. This is because the way you feel on the inside greatly determines the way you experience life on the outside.

When you're having a bad day, you are feeling off on that day. Due to already feeling off, you are more easily distressed by life around you. Therefore, how you already feel on the inside is easily stirred up by the daily interactions or life around you, causing you to feel your distress even more. You could react and blame someone or life around you or you could learn to recognise, that it is just *being you* that feels off, and that life around you is merely stimulating and is not causing, how it already feels inside of you.

On these days, if you could contain and live with the feeling of you rather than blame the world around you, this would dramatically reduce your distress. It's not the world's fault. It's nobody's fault. It's just how you feel today. The point is, however you feel on the inside can and usually will determine how you interpret and experience life around you and therefore whether or not you like your life today.

DETERMINING THE QUALITY OF YOUR LIFE

Even if it is someone or something unpleasant in the world around you that is disturbing you, reacting to that will potentially consume you. If you want to save yourself from tons of misery derived from the *effects* of reacting, the solution, which is what *really* matters to you, depends entirely on recognising yourself reacting and knowing how to resolve it there, within you.

Can you see that the way it already feels inside of you each day can determine how you experience and react to life on the outside, the world you work in or the people you are connected to?

Can you also see how very easy it is for us to assume or mistakenly think that other people and life around us are making us feel the way we do, when the fact is, these are only stimulating whatever is already going on inside us that day? How we respond to all this, firstly to what is inside us and secondly to life outside us is of crucial importance, for that response will determine our quality of life.

Not knowing how to deal with the problem of reactionary behaviour is the *real* problem, whilst knowing how to, is the solution for navigating everyday difficulties in your life.

But just *knowing* about the mechanics of reaction is not always enough. You also need to *feel* the sensation of reaction within you, as it is happening, and the next section of this chapter will get you doing this. When you have both knowing and sensing in the heat of life, *then* you will have the foundational capacity to diffuse distress and navigate problems whenever you need to.

WHAT CAUSES REACTIONS?

When the way you are thinking is causing you distress, it is reactionary thinking. If it is enabling you to flow with life, it is responsive thinking.

Reactionary thinking is loaded with pain and learned rigidities and so is resistant to life. Responsive thinking is free of these and so is more intelligent, receptive and intuitive. As you heal whatever is driving or causing you to react, your access to this receptive intelligence for life will increase, making life easier and so your distress in life decreases.

1. The First and Least Complex Cause of Reaction is General Preferences

Have you noticed how disturbance from your casual objection to a daily fact of life occurs simply because the fact doesn't fit with your preferences? These types of general preferences are of minor importance to you and the disturbance they cause is not so deep, yet ultimately, they cause you to clash with the realities of life and increase your stress in every day life. To resolve this distress, you do not need to think more about it. Rather, you simply need to go beneath all this thinking, into the deeper physical sense of the stress it causes in your body.

By feeling the stress that your preferences cause in your body you will enable it to dissipate, and the sense of importance you place on your preferences, which you feel driving you, will also lessen.

Throughout your day, take notice whenever your preferences over one thing or another drive you to react, and experiment with resolving these for yourself. This may seem a small thing, but over the course of a day it will significantly decrease your accumulation of stress.

2. The Second and More Complex Cause of Reaction is Overpowering Beliefs That Claim Your True Identity

This type of reaction has greater severity than those caused by general preferences due to its basis in more biased beliefs developed from unresolved past experiences, religious or cultural beliefs or beliefs about how you or others should be. These beliefs are more deeply impressed or imposed upon you, and they make up a false identity, an artificial sort of self-importance, and so have greater power and influence over you. They also cause you to feel more justified in your clash with others and support your denial of the realities of life wherever these don't conform to or fit in with your beliefs. This inevitably causes greater distress for you and others than general preferences or opinions do.

If you can realise how your biases or beliefs do not make your life with others easier but in fact complicate and make our lives together more difficult, it is then easier to drop any petty beliefs. Then, uninhibited by beliefs, you are set free to attune to the more important needs and challenges we all face in life, and with this deeper maturity you can relate more with others and live life more effectively.

This will massively reduce the cause of your own reactions and distress.

3. The Third Most Complex Cause of Reaction is from Distress, Pain or Trauma Held Within You

Abusive treatment from others throughout your life forms into the way you feel about and within yourself. This determines how you think about yourself, treat yourself and allow others to treat you. When your reaction is fuelled from these more serious personal traumas, you may find yourself suffering extreme intolerance. You may be easily angered or frightened, enraged or depressed, for no apparent reason.

You probably have a very good reason for feeling this way, however, it may not be so much what you are reacting *to* in your life now but what is boiling up from deeper within you that is disturbing you. You will find some relief and less suffering if you return your attention to *how it feels to be you,* in the unresolved trauma felt in your body, rather than *think* (stew and fume) about anything outside of you that is triggering your reaction.

Once you have a deeper sense of yourself in the body, however that feels, you will be less likely to mentally react to inner disturbances or outer triggers in life. You will be more able to naturally absorb and dissipate distress just by feeling it in your body throughout the course of your day. The more regularly you sit physically still, without concern for your thinking, but just feeling all sensations of and in your body, the further you will establish this solid foundational sense of yourself in the body.

Notice whenever you become intolerant, irritated, impatient or angry, frightened or depressed, without a logical or reasonable reason for it. Don't connect these feelings with your life now. Instead of agreeing with these feelings, validating, justifying or excusing the reason for feeling this way, just feel it, staying with that as a feeling in your body. Be wary of the stories you think up to support or justify you feeling in any way bad. As an experiment, rather than buying into these stories, stop them, diffuse them by focusing into the feelings they have caused, wherever that is in your body, and give it time to dissipate inside of you.

MASTERING YOUR REACTIONS

Whatever happens in life has an effect on you. Without understanding reactions, you will not be able to fully process and recover from many of these effects. It is their accumulation that causes your mental and physical health to deteriorate more rapidly as you age. But with this understanding you will be more able to process and resolve anything that life throws at you. You will therefore strengthen, deepen and evolve through life, prolonging your health and your natural life span.

Using the active meditations in the Undo app will develop a capacity within you, which will form into a natural ability to recognise and sense the difference between what is inside you and what is coming at you from life around you, and therefore not be so influenced or affected by life, and also recognise and sense when you are reacting and to stay in touch with the reaction inside of you and resolve it there. This will help prevent you creating or getting caught up in unnecessary or prolonged conflict with others or the world around you.

If you only gain this one understanding and skill from Undo, you will find it making a huge difference in every area of your life now and for the rest of your life. As you master reactions, you will more clearly see and understand the effects that life has had on you, and all of your relationships will become clearer and more understandable. You will also find that any stressful, hurtful or harmful situation will be resolvable. Through this crucial understanding, all of life will be revealed as a source of your own self-discovery and personal development.

To progress further with this requires a clear understanding of feeling. What it is to truly feel, how to feel and the necessity of feeling. Thinking is not feeling. Emotion is not feeling. Without purely feeling, thinking and emotion accumulate and actually prolong tension and distress beyond their natural duration, and so become harmful to your physical and mental health. In the upcoming chapter, you will discover how thinking and emotion prolong suffering and how feeling ends it. Only by purely feeling can you relieve your system of overthinking and emotionalising, and in this way naturally end your distress or pain before further harm occurs. But you won't be able to do this until you understand how to truly feel, which is why the next chapter is all about Feeling.

Go to the Active Meditations for this chapter in the Undo app.

PONDER YOUR PROGRESS

Do you now see how your annoyance with the world around you begins within you?

Have you begun to see that the way you are affected by others comes back to how you feel or think about yourself, and how this can be resolved inside of you?

Have you noticed any change in your ability to handle distressing situations or people?

Feel free to note any changes that you can see in yourself… subtle changes are often the deepest changes. The deepest changes are often unknown to us at the time of change and are instead only known to us as the improvements in our physical condition and the reduction of our disturbances with real life situations. So take some time out to ponder that.

NOTES:

_____

_____

_____

_____

_____

_____

_____

_____

_____

_____

_____

CHAPTER THREE
FEELINGS

IN THE PREVIOUS TOPICS, you learned about think-ing and its confusing effects when it is in reaction to anything at all, as well as how to diffuse and resolve your thought-reactions by going deeper into the feelings of distress driving these. Now you will learn a lot more about feelings and their separate purpose to thinking.

There is a significant difference between emotion and feeling. Emotion is not feeling.

It is essential to remove the confusion of emotion from feeling in order to sense and know what you actually feel.

Do you know what it is to feel or do you only think your feelings?

It is the purpose of deeper feelings to enable your under-standing of you—however you are at any moment. You feel sad which is how you know you are sad. You feel hunger and so know you are hungry. You do not know these things or yourself through thought. That is what feeling is for.

CHECK IN WITH YOURSELF

Do you know the difference between feeling and emotion?

Have you ever tried just feeling your distress to recover from it—rather than thinking about it and stressing over it?

Note your answers and then put them aside whilst you complete this chapter. At the end there will be a review of these questions to highlight your progress and help you realise the changes that have naturally happened within you in this process.

UNDERSTANDING THE PURPOSE OF FEELING

Although we put a lot of importance on our thinking, we have tried to rely on it for more than it is intended and therefore, have relied on it for more than we really can. When we are unaware that *feeling* is our source of understanding ourselves, we substitute feeling with analysing or thinking in an attempt to understand ourselves and then become confused.

Thinking can describe a feeling but is incapable of actually feeling. Thinking can only describe what we already understand as a feeling and from feeling that feeling. Feeling occurs at a deeper level within ourselves than thinking can go. It is important to recognise that thought or thinking is not the source of understanding or a method to understand ourselves. Feeling is.

Compared to feeling, thinking is shallow or superficial. Only the body feels. However, thinking can and does affect how we experience our feelings and how we interpret the understanding of ourselves that they provide.

Thinking about and emotionalising our feelings by judging or complaining about them prolongs feelings beyond what would otherwise be their natural lifespan. Prolonged feelings build up into distress held in the body. Then this physical distress drives our mental distress and confusion. Unresolved and prolonged over time it escalates into physical and mental illnesses.

To feel, is a live physical function. Only the body feels, as only the body is alive. Thought is neither alive nor a function for feeling or sensing. It is an expression of and driven by these but it is only a mechanical function in itself.

CHANGING YOUR LIFE BY LEARNING TO FEEL

Whenever you feel held back, stuck, driven, frightened or frustrated, whenever you think or feel you can't do something or just sense something is stopping you, you need to focus into the *feel* of what is stopping you, into the sense of that. You will find that it is a sensation in your body existing beneath any thinking or reactionary concerns with the way you are. It's from in here, in how you feel, that it rules you. Don't fight it at all. No matter how disturbing or painful or annoying, feel it as it is anyway. That's how it will dissipate and decrease in its effect on you. Bit by bit it will change and you will be free of it.

We can live our whole lives unable to change even though we want to, even if the way we are is harmful to ourselves or others. Why is that? Because we don't know how to truly feel and so we don't truly *feel* anything. We avoid feeling what we really need to. We avoid the truth of ourselves by avoiding anything that makes us feel uncomfortable or distressed. This is why and how we have forgotten what it is to feel and so why we cannot change, even when we want to.

Change in life begins with you feeling and thereby resolving or healing whatever is inside you, including that which you may not want to feel. When you understand that feeling *all* feelings, including stressful painful feelings, rather than avoiding them, is how they will change, you appreciate their importance and feel them rather than avoid them.

This need to feel is as universal as our need to sleep and eat. The need feeling fulfils is the same for all of us. However, feeling is not a mental state but a purely physical sensation. When you truly feel, the underlying energy of your unresolved feelings dissipates, then the mental states and habits or actions that originate in these feelings, and that dominate you, will fall away and cease to continue.

CLARIFYING REACTION AND FEELING

On the surface is your thinking. Beneath that is solely feeling. When you are reacting to the world outside of you, that reaction distorts your view and experience of the world and causes you confusion and misery.

Similarly, when you are reacting to what you *feel* within you, your thought-reaction distorts your view and experience of whatever you feel inside. Again, it is reactionary thought that is causing any confusion or misery, and not the reality of your actual feeling.

Whether directed towards the outside world or directed towards the feeling of you on the inside, reactionary thinking distorts, falsifies and confuses your experience of that.

SIMPLIFYING FEELING AND EMOTION

Emotion is not feeling. It is the distortion caused when what you think about a feeling is imposed on and mixed with what you actually feel below the surface of your thinking. This reaction of your thinking, which is your thought description and bias against the actual pure feeling, creates an entirely different experience to that within the original pure feeling. When reactionary thinking occurs, the beneficial potential of the original pure feeling is lost. It is important to understand this, for whenever a feeling, disturbing or otherwise, is felt as it is, the benefit is that the felt disturbance naturally and gradually dissipates, leaving the body free of accumulated tension or distress.

But once your thought-reaction to a feeling interferes, this creates emotionalism and your connection with the real feeling is lost to the dramatics of this thought-feeling mix of emotion. Emotion then perpetuates itself, accumulating as stress and tension that's harmful to the body and causing all types of mental distress and confusion.

The effects of this thought-feeling mix called emotion results in exaggeration of and desensitisation to the actual feeling. To emotionalise is in fact another reactionary condition. Specifically, emotion is a reaction to feeling how you truly feel and is an avoidance of that feeling.

Whether we avoid the facts of an external event or situation, or avoid and deny a feeling within us, we are avoiding a true fact of life and overwhelming ourselves with the emotion we cause through doing this.

For instance, if we lose someone to death or otherwise, and if we accept that fact, we are left with a pure and appropriate feeling of loss. In time that feeling dissolves harmlessly and we are healed from feeling that way, free to move on with our life no longer hindered by the loss. But if we don't accept that *fact of our loss,* we keep thinking about how it shouldn't have happened and how it could be if we hadn't lost them. By adding and indulging in this endless story, we avoid the true fact and feeling of a loss in life, we mix that story with the real feeling of loss and create and suffer *emotion.*

This emotional reaction to the true fact of our loss and not the loss itself causes our suffering—our suffering is not of the loss but of our emotionalised distortion in reaction to our loss.

Facing the truth of either a circumstance, or just feeling the way you truly do brings an end to emotion. Otherwise there is no end. Your reactionary thinking of your complaints and objections to life being as it is or was, creates its own false and dead form of feeling in emotion. As emotions are reactionary thought based and disconnected from the truth which you don't want to face, feel or accept, there is no way for that emotion to end, and most importantly there is no way for your pain to end.

As far as the body is concerned, one feeling or sensation is as significant as another. As you understand this more, you will realise that there are no good or bad feelings, only different feelings conveying different information. Only our reactionary thinking (our emotionally charged imagination, beliefs or biases) makes them seem and feel good or bad. This causes us to overlook the unique significance of each feeling or sensation, and their purpose in being our primary and immediate source of understanding ourselves and our needs.

Emotion is not feeling. It is story-based dramatisation causing overwhelment with life. Emotion and feeling have very different results. Emotion prolongs suffering. Feeling ends it.

Emotion is predominantly a reactionary mental function and dramatisation which overrides and destroys our capacity to think sanely or truly feel. It dominates and taints our mental state and prevents our acceptance and resolution of disturbances from life events and our capacity to move on.

Feeling is entirely a function of and in the body. When we simply physically feel our feelings, they proceed to dissipate and the body is relieved of the effects left from day-to-day existence. This dissipation, relief and natural ending of all and any feeling, pleasurable, painful or distressing, is essential to maintaining optimal health.

So far you have progressed from reactionary thinking to truly feeling. As you can see, feelings are a very important part of our makeup and an intrinsic part of being able to recover and heal. To expand your understanding of feelings, the next chapter is about Senses where you will learn to find fulfilment and contentment readily accessible and already available within you.

Go to the Active Meditations for this chapter in the Undo app.

PONDER YOUR PROGRESS

Are you any more interested in your feelings now?

Are you starting to understand the difference between emotion and purely feeling?

Have you noticed any change in your distress, now that you are shifting from stressing over it to feeling it more?

Are your emotions dissipating more easily now?

Feel free to note any changes that you can see in yourself… subtle changes are often the deepest changes. The deepest changes are often unknown to us at the time of change and are instead only known to us as the improvements in our physical condition and the reduction of our disturbances with real life situations. So take some time out to ponder that.

NOTES:

_____

_____

_____

_____

_____

_____

_____

_____

_____

_____

CHAPTER FOUR
SENSES

PREVIOUSLY YOU LEARNED ABOUT feeling. Now you will be expanding that understanding to include and fully benefit from the complete use of your feelings and senses in your daily life.

Our living experience—what we sense or feel in daily life—significantly determines our degree of fulfilment and our general sense of our self. No amount of trying to get what we want through the cleverness of thinking can replace or provide what is readily and only available to us through our senses.

CHECK IN WITH YOURSELF

Do you know what your senses are for?

What they feel like when they are in use?

Note your answers and then put them aside whilst you complete this chapter. At the end there will be a review of these questions to highlight your progress and help you realise the changes that have naturally happened within you in this process.

SENSING AS THE BASIS OF FULFILMENT

When your senses are fully alert, receptive to sound, sight, smell, taste or the touch of the whole surface of your skin, then the entire inside of you comes to life. Through sensing, the whole body of you comes into connection with the world outside your skin. Only in this sensory connection and sensation of *you* can you experience the fulfilment of the whole *felt sense* of you and everything else.

When sensing, thought drops into its natural quiet background rhythm, and as intended, only responds to the tangible and mechanical demands of daily life. With only mechanical thought remaining, thinking no longer drowns out the sensory wholeness of our living experience.

Our living experience—what we sense or feel in daily life—significantly determines our degree of fulfilment or emptiness, satisfaction or dissatisfaction and our general sense of how we feel being our self. Beginning with the initial sensory response of a particular external sense organ, other internal systems follow—hormonal, nervous and more—involving our body's entire sensory response to daily stimulation. This activation of any sense organ is literally our coming to life within. The cumulative sensations of this determines our fundamental experience of life.

Secondary to and once removed from this *felt sense* of life is what we think about in reaction to either the external activity we are involved in or to what is felt as it comes to life within us. This thinking, being once removed from what is felt, desensitises us partially or completely, depending on how much thinking there is and how intense or distracting that thinking is.

Essentially, the amount of thinking or the reactionary intensity of that thinking directly affects our capacity to feel alive and be fulfilled in life. The less we think, the more deeply alive we are able to feel and the more completely we engage and come to life, both in ourselves and in sensory connection to whatever we interact with externally. However, we tend to overlook, even ignore, the perpetual activity of our senses because as a de-naturalised species, we have come to rely on an overuse of our thinking to get or achieve what we *think* we want in life.

But no amount of thinking can achieve the fulfilment that is only available to us through our senses.

RESENSITISING AND FEELING MORE ALIVE

We need thought to function mechanically and achieve necessities in life but the *fulfilment* we seek is defined by how those achievements leave us feeling. Curiously, all we *really* seek is a feeling of fulfilment or satisfaction from what we do or have in life, without which we lose interest and quickly move on to the next attempt at fulfilment.

Even if we find no lasting resolution for our dissatisfaction, once we are shallow and removed from our live sense of things, it is difficult to return from that. When we are swept up in the momentum of endless pursuits and deadening thinking, we are oblivious to our sensory fulfilment, which is only available to us when we slow down enough to sense or feel it activated by whatever flows in through the living senses of our body.

When we are numbed or oblivious to this readily available resource and deep sense of fulfilment, we try to get more out of life through artificial or thought-based pleasure. Then we start searching for sensory exaggerations through inventive or imaginative thinking to try to feel something more. This only numbs us further to the natural occurrence of fulfilment.

As the solution for fulfilment is already there in our body, there is no need to pursue or purpose in pursuing fulfilment. It is already happening naturally and for real, as a part of every felt-sensed stimulation in your body. You simply need attune to this.

Doesn't it make more sense to notice, attune to and benefit from that which is readily available, rather than exhaust yourself with pursuits for something you already have, but simply overlook?

When we are desensitised to our naturally occurring sensory fulfilment, we try to achieve fulfilment externally. There is clearly a paradox here. That is, any attempt to achieve fulfilment—which only occurs when we are unfulfilled—happens as a result of us being desensitised and once removed from all of our already felt fulfilment. Therefore, as long as you remain desensitised, all true fulfilment is impossible. Ironically, any pursuit or action driven from this can only continue a sense of lack or emptiness, because the pursuit is both the cause of and desensitisation from what is readily available in the first place.

RECONNECTING TO YOUR SENSES

When you listen to the ocean and only receive—not think about, its sound, that sound fills and satisfies in a way only hearing that sound can.

When you gaze upon a scene, only when you do not think about, describe or analyse it can you receive it fully as it is, and in that purely sensory act, feel connected and filled with the scene itself.

When you taste your food, the pleasure or satisfaction of that fulfils you in that moment, an action entirely dependent on your sense of taste alone. Thought can add nothing real to the sense experience and nothing needs to be added. It fulfils just as it is.

When your skin touches another's, or feels the heat of the sun or a hot bath, if you really are only feeling the sensation and not thinking about it, then the simple direct living experience brings you to life, in a felt sense of you, fully connected in and fulfilled by that moment.

LIVING LIFE BY SENSING LIFE

Any analysing or describing what you sense depletes, distracts from and lessens the sense experience essential for fulfilment and satisfaction in life. If you romanticise these acts of life or trivialise them into a pleasure seeking technique, you risk overlooking entirely the significance and importance in this to all of us. For what is life without pure sensation or feeling? Is it life at all? What is it that prevents fulfilment and satisfaction coming freely and effortlessly to you daily? It is your unnecessary thinking about everything that causes your oblivion to the fulfilment available in all that you sense or feel.

You cannot capture and keep this fulfilment you feel. Nor do you need to. For once the fulfilment of sensation passes, another is freely and readily available, in and from the next event in life. You neither need to strive for this nor try to keep it. In your direct sense of life, fulfilment and satisfaction are always a part of living.

Taking for granted and overlooking the essential value of this continuous active-animal function has added to the desensitisation of our de-naturalised existence. Fortunately it is still there, functioning in you all day, every day. But you have to stop thinking so much and slow down in your activity. Take enough time in each act to notice and appreciate each of your senses at their initial physical point of activation, before you go off into the deadened world of your thinking.

Your senses have a far greater role and significance in your being fulfilled than you will at first realise or appreciate. That is, until you experiment with this and find out from yourself.

So far, you have built a solid new foundation for your life combining reactions, feelings and senses. With this new sense of yourself, in the next chapter we dive into Natural Intelligence where you'll deepen the use of your full body intelligence to help you navigate life as a unique individual.

Go to the Active Meditations for this chapter in the Undo app.

PONDER YOUR PROGRESS

Has there been any change in your contentment with yourself?

Did you set out to change these things or did they just happen on their own, simply by you hearing this information and completing this chapter?

Feel free to note any changes that you can see in yourself... subtle changes are often the deepest changes. The deepest changes are often unknown to us at the time of change and are instead only known to us as the improvements in our physical condition and the reduction of our disturbances with real life situations. So take some time out to ponder that.

NOTES:

_____

_____

_____

_____

_____

_____

_____

_____

_____

_____

CHAPTER FIVE
NATURAL INTELLIGENCE

P REVIOUSLY YOU LEARNED ABOUT feeling, sensation and your sensory connection to life outside
you, and today you'll be learning how they combine to form
your whole body Natural Intelligence.

Natural intelligence is a whole body, sense-based intelligence that dwarfs and precedes all thinking. The body
understands through sensing what the intellectual processes
of thought can only interpret and describe. The body is alive
and so it is an interconnected part of the whole of life. The
body is life understanding itself moment by moment. Unlike
thinking, which becomes obsolete and biased overtime, the
felt or sensed information of natural intelligence is an immediate response of the body to all of life. Then, once received
and made use of, that information fades away leaving a clean
slate to feel, sense and understand the next moment in life
without bias. Awakening to your natural intelligence, you sink
beneath adopted or imposed ideas and experience life in an
entirely different way, as it really is, and unique to you alone.

CHECK IN WITH YOURSELF

Remember back to what you were like when you started reading this book. What changes in your life or your approach to life have happened since you began?

Are you using your feelings and senses more to understand yourself and to know life around you?

Note your answers and then put them aside whilst you complete this chapter. At the end there will be a review of these questions to highlight your progress and help you realise the changes that have naturally happened within you in this process.

USING YOUR NATURAL INTELLIGENCE TO NAVIGATE LIFE

Like your own sonar for life, your natural intelligence originates as the initial physical alert and sensed understanding of your environment to inform and protect you. If you pay attention, you will regularly notice your felt sense operating either as a subtle or obvious disturbance for example, when someone is lying to you. You may be mentally convinced when under their direct influence, but then later when alone you have a conflicting feeling which won't let you trust them. You may not know why, you just can't, your felt sense won't let you. Your body cannot accept a lie easily but your thought process often can't tell either way, as it relies solely on your limit of knowledge on the topic the person is talking about.

However, even when the topic is one you know little or nothing about, the body can still feel a disturbance, a wrongness, a misalignment with its own intrinsic survival ability to sense when something simply *is not right*. You can't explain it, but you can sense it and you know.

In fact, this felt sensed intelligence functions in every area and every moment of your life. Without it you simply cannot function effectively, safely or intelligently.

FUNCTIONING FROM YOUR NATURAL INTELLIGENCE

There is a common misunderstanding of the purpose of physical feelings or sensations that leads to a preference for pleasurable feelings and the avoidance of painful feelings or disturbance. The simple truth is, the whole range of sensations, from pleasure through to pain, are all equally significant and necessary conveyors of information in our lives. Through their variety is how different types of information are conveyed and recognised by the living organism of you! Even the lack of a single sensation would be a cause for concern, for that would mean our ability to recognise and understand all that sensation conveys would be missing.

One feeling does not convey what another can. So, each sen-
sation is necessary for our capacity for intelligence to be complete.

In fact, one could safely say that it is more crucial to
notice pain than pleasure—what we don't want over what
we do want—if we are to ensure that we avoid disaster and
suffering. Fully considering feeling's actual purpose in our
lives, we come to realise and accept that our having preference
for one sensation over another, or for feeling one way over
another, is only due to a shallow view and poor appreciation
of the full purpose of feeling or sensation.

Variations in the *feeling* of us occur due to the continual
variation in the information conveyed at this primary level,
including a variety of disturbances, all of which are required
as alerts to all we need to know to survive each day.

Avoiding disturbing feelings is dangerous, for disturbing
feelings alert us to potential harm so that we may avoid that
harm. Pursuing only pleasure and avoiding disturbance is a
blind and disastrous approach to life that eventuates in reoccurring pain and distress, and maintains the same ignorance
of why the pain and distress occur. Life isn't supposed to be
a conundrum. All that you need to alter course in your life
is sourced from the sensations of intelligence originating in
your body.

These sensations are always guiding us. Pleasure or neu-
trality informs us all is okay, pain or distress alerts us that
something is wrong or about to become so. Every situation
in your life, every moment in your life, your inherent natural intelligence is operating automatically. Every species of
animal relies on this function for its survival and its sensed

navigation through every step of its life, and in this we animals are no different.

GROUNDING YOUR INTELLIGENCE IN SENSATIONS

As far as the body is concerned, one feeling or sensation is
as significant as another. As you understand this more, you
will realise that there are no good or bad feelings, that only
our reactionary thinking, our imagination and beliefs or bias
make them seem and feel good or bad. This categorisation
of sensation causes us to overlook the significance of each
unique feeling or sensation, which is simply that they convey
different information.

As you have learned so far, all feelings or sensations are
the body's source of information about itself and about life
outside our skin, and that these felt or sensed facts of information are our primary and needed guides in life.

At the most basic level and vital to our survival, it is
only through our physical sensations that we can receive
the information we need, to know about our *external* world,
such as whether it is hot or cold, dangerous or safe and so
on. Equally, to understand our *internal* world and ourselves,
we primarily rely on feelings.

Hunger and thirst, for example, are internal feelings
generated from physical sensations. Through thinking alone,
we cannot know what hunger or thirst is. Only through our
feelings can we understand how *we* are, whether we are sad

or cold or sick or in pain, tired, frightened or at ease. And from these feelings we understand ourselves and our needs. This is what feeling is for.

DEEPLY UNDERSTANDING YOUR BODY—YOUR LIFE

The body understands in a different manner to thinking or intellect. The function of thinking or intellect in fact does not understand at all, it merely accepts or rejects information dependent on preferences and on information initially gained from the body sensing. Through our thinking, we can only interpret all these sensations and make mechanical decisions on the purely practical issues in life. That is all thought can do and when we try to use it for understanding ourselves, the best we can do with thought is form opinions based on our preferences, so we become confused about the facts—facts which are initially gained from physical sensations and via our senses.

As feeling is an intelligence specifically for understanding yourself and knowing your needs, the information in our feelings can be more personal than that in the more basic sensations. Like sensation, feeling is also a bodily sensation that precedes the thoughts that can only describe the understanding already held within that feeling.

As a living organism we are completely reliant on the integrity of our sensations and sensing for our survival and wellbeing. This is the reason why bodily sensation or sensing is completely and inherently uncensored, raw and unbias and therefore true to whatever the body senses, even if it's about yourself. That is why you can always trust your body, and primarily is why your body cannot lie. To lie would be to harm itself which it cannot naturally do, and neither is self-harm aligned with its primary purpose and urge to live.

Sensation and the information held as sensations in the body precedes thought and yet is the origin of true thinking. Meaning, thinking that is a true representation or expression of us and a true indication of the body's needs.

But essentially feeling and sensation are the same—both are live physical sensations on which we are reliant to understand ourselves, form thoughts from, motivate action and navigate our way through life.

This natural function of feeling has been ignored, distorted and minimalised in its use due to our over reliance on thinking, leading to our belief in the fictitious separation between a mind and a body. Our common belief in this fictitious separation is responsible for our desensitisation, confusions and capacity for harm.

You have now reached a turning point in the flow of Undo. You have established a new foundation of feeling for understanding yourself. You have also learned that you can rely more on your body's language of physical sensation to guide yourself through life. You have begun to break down your over-reliance on thinking to get you through life.

Now you are discovering the combination of feeling and sensing to be your Natural Intelligence and new foundation for navigating your way through life.

To continue on with your self-understanding, from here we go into the next chapter on Beliefs. You will need that information to help you overcome the limitations beliefs have on your full potential and open yourself to the discovery of the real you!

Go to the Active Meditations for this chapter in the Undo app.

PONDER YOUR PROGRESS

What do you feel are the greatest benefits you've got from reading this book?

What realisations have you had along the way?

Feel free to note any changes that you can see in yourself… subtle changes are often the deepest changes. The deepest changes are often unknown to us at the time of change and are instead only known to us as the improvements in our physical condition and the reduction of our disturbances with real life situations. So take some time out to ponder that.

NOTES:

CHAPTER SIX
BELIEF

W ELCOME BACK, TODAY YOU'LL BE learning about beliefs. The mechanical use of beliefs is their only intended and correct use. In this section we expose how the facts are sufficient for life, and how adding our personal bias or belief systems to life is a problematic misuse of beliefs that only distorts or confuses our life. Let's get started on beliefs.

Belief is fake knowing. Repeated over time, belief creates an illusion, making you feel as though you know something when you really don't. Believing something is not knowing, and the belief itself prevents you from admitting or even realising what you don't know. If you truly know, you don't require belief—you know.

To admit not knowing something is the first step to opening yourself up to new discoveries of what is yet unknown to you, which is no small thing.

CHECK IN WITH YOURSELF

Do you understand what a belief is?

Did you know there is a difference between factual mechanical beliefs that are necessary for functioning in everyday life and other types of beliefs?

Note your answers and then put them aside whilst you complete this chapter. At the end there will be a review of these questions to highlight your progress and help you realise the changes that have naturally happened within you in this process.

HOW BELIEFS PREVENT HUMAN CONNECTION

Have you ever noticed how, when we meet someone, we chat for a while, getting familiar, all seems comfortable and agreeable then we reach a certain point where a personal view or belief is touched on and we tense up or clash. Something happens inside us that causes us to resist or judge that person's view or we might feel a slight annoyance or disagreement kick in. We may then feel angry or fearful depending on our nature or the rigidity of our beliefs.

Two outcomes usually result from this situation. In one, we push through this resistance or disagreement. As a result, we possibly alter our position, learn something more or let something go and finally relax and connect comfortably once again and the relationship continues. Alternatively, we internally withdraw and hold firm to our opinion whilst avoiding or skirting around the topic from then on. We may even decide the other person is stupid, ignorant or arrogant and end the conversation or interaction there. The point is, all goes well as long as they think along similar lines, believing or thinking the same ideas we do.

So what has happened here?

We have come upon the effects of our own limiting beliefs or bias and at that point, the protective aggression or intensity of our beliefs ends the flow of the social connection. At this point, we pull back and isolate into the fixed position of our own bias or belief structures.

We take on beliefs or ideas as substitutes for our lack of knowledge when we are not comfortable with not knowing. Knowing is dynamic because what we know and need to know changes as we change and as life around us changes, but beliefs and ideas are static. Beliefs don't change which means that when we adopt them, they become our fixed view point and determine the way we think and live from that point on. They become part of us. We feel as though we know what we only believe, and form a false sense of ourself based on this fake knowing. This is how we identify with belief.

These beliefs or learned ideas are the wedges causing division, withdrawal and varying degrees of stagnation in both new and long-standing human interactions the world over.

Now, what if it is *the other person's* fixed ideas or beliefs that have emerged in the course of an interaction, and not yours? If it is not *your* beliefs interfering, then you will be less likely to feel annoyed, aggressive or defensive, or have the need to assert or impose your ideas. You may sense a wall in the other person which you cannot break through that prevents any real or unguarded connection. This can be frustrating because we naturally want to connect. However, this is the effect of beliefs; they prevent our human connection, prevent us from understanding one another or ourselves as we really are, and separate us from the natural world in general.

Beliefs also prevents our receptivity and discovery of anything outside of the limited boundaries of our beliefs. In this way, beliefs significantly reduce our capacity for further intelligence.

UNDERSTANDING HOW WE MISUSE BELIEF

Purely mechanical thinking or belief that is used for the practicality of living our lives doesn't cause this problem of losing touch with yourself. But when we misuse thought to invent beliefs to define ourselves by, we create ideas and beliefs *about* ourselves which we then identify with as being ourselves. This divides us from our natural and inherent sense of ourselves in our body. Identified with and lost in these various beliefs about our self, we lose touch with our common, felt sense deeper in our body, and our shared common ground, our shared humanity.

It is important to understand that what you identify with is always separate to you. It is not you. It's only a belief or idea that you add to or impose upon your true self. Curiously, you do not identify with yourself—you are yourself. But when you identify with things or ideas you lose touch with what it is to be you. And that is where the problem begins.

These beliefs, which each of us portray as ourselves then cause imaginary conflict between us. I say imaginary because the conflict is not between our true selves, but between these divided beliefs which we identify with, lose ourselves in and then clash with each other over. But because all beliefs are equally fantastic and insubstantial, there is no way to end the conflict other than to realise that conflict is only between what we have imagined and then believed in. Otherwise, as living organisms or natural people without belief-based identities, we relate to and understand one another and have no basis for prolonged conflict with each other.

This misuse of belief, of forming beliefs about ourselves, is not what belief is intended for. As a result, it produces side effects of feelings of insecurity and uncertainty, and an underlying sense of lacking or false sense of superiority, whilst at the same time denying or covering all this over. Out of this lacking, we feel a need to compensate further by asserting these *self-defining* ideas over one another in an attempt to be something more than we honestly feel or think we are. For beliefs always secretly harbour doubts and the potential for disbelief, and these hidden insecurities cause a drive to assert ourselves over others. This is why beliefs become the seeds of aggression, violence and war.

WHAT IS BELIEF REALLY FOR?

The correct and basic use of belief is for the practicality of living which is all we need it for and is its only intended use. No harm comes of the intended use of belief. I ask you how old you are, you tell me, and I *believe* you. As I cannot know, I have to rely on you to tell me. This works perfectly if you don't lie and well enough even if you do. It is often the best we can do. We are reliant on this mechanical, intended and true use of belief to function together.

We expect and believe the information we receive from each other to be real and true. Yet, when we ask for information from someone we know the potential for lies or mistakes exist and so we still think for ourselves or find out for ourselves, depending on the importance of the accuracy of information. But we expect that information refers to and is backed up by existing facts, not no-thing at all as is the case of fantasy, belief systems and ideologies.

Although these mechanical beliefs are just information that we believe for the convenience of navigating our practical life, information still needs to be about or describe something real for it to be meaningful or information at all. Otherwise it is meaningless, it is not informing us of anything so cannot be called information. It is nothing at all. Just gibberish.

Our basic use of belief for communicating practical information between us is convenient and even necessary for day to day life, simply because we cannot always know everything we need to. But this information is always about or referring to something real. If we find out it is not, we call that a lie or a delusion and dismiss it as misinformation and consider ourselves fooled. If we can't prove it true for ourselves, we accept it may not be true. Until we can confirm it either way, often through more information or our own experience, we remain unconcluded. We are not depending on it to define ourselves, we know it is just mechanical information and so we don't make it personal or become personally dependent on it.

An example of informative mechanical beliefs is when physicians tell us what they know about the inside of the human body. We choose to believe them, yet without attending an autopsy we don't actually know for ourselves. We often forget that even if we read something in a book, that is still second hand and only believed by us. There are many things like this, harmless and convenient to believe, which we expect to inform us of something real.

Whereas with fantasy there is no such requirement. It doesn't matter that it is made up, because it is about nothing real and we do not expect it to be believed. We all agree it is only for entertainment. And anyone believing fantasy as real we understand has lost touch with reality and is possibly delusional.

DEFINING FACT AND FANTASY

When we adopt a belief system to define ourselves or all of existence, we neglect to establish our own confirmation of whether it is factual, and therefore knowable, or a fiction, and therefore unknowable, then blindly make conclusions and dangerously proceed on that basis without our own confirmation.

But the blind faith of *believing in* something is actually believing in nothing, especially if the thing believed in doesn't actually exist. This is a completely different use and meaning of the word belief. With this use of belief, the existence of a fact or true information or object, is not required. There is a description but what is described doesn't actually exist. It is only in the words, in the thoughts themselves, just ideas. Nothing exists beyond those ideas to be described by those ideas. This is the definition of fantasy. If we identify with or believe a fantasy to be real, we dissociate from reality and can lose ourselves in whatever we have made up.

When people use this fantasy form of belief to define themselves and the universe, they become confused. The power in this form of belief is to believe that you are something you are not, to view the world other than how it is and to imagine things that are not there. Great harm comes of this because belief is not for defining yourself and when you try to use it for this purpose, you only confuse and lose yourself.

You only try to define yourself with belief when you have a diminished or no sense of yourself as you are, or don't wish to accept yourself as you are. It is pretending to know and a form of escapism from what you don't want to know.

This is how we trick ourselves or others, and how the propagation of belief systems have been used to diminish peoples' ability to think truthfully and for themselves. Using belief for fantasy, imagination and escapism is very different to the mechanical practical use of belief and is very harmful.

This misuse of belief is for fooling others and yourself, and blinds its user to any *obvious proof* of the non-existence of what you believe in.

KNOWING WHEN TO USE BELIEF

The prerequisite for any system of belief is the non-existence of what is believed in, otherwise it would not be a system of belief but a description of known and knowable facts. Even to believe yourself superior requires you feeling lesser as the prerequisite driving your interest in being defined as or believing your superiority. This self-definition is a fantasy that compensates for whatever is missing or lacking. Once again showing, the absence of what is believed in precedes and necessitates your belief.

Taken for granted and accepted without realising its significance is that—*if* it exists it is not believed but known. Only if it doesn't exist can believing in it be applicable and even possible. What exists is knowable or known. What doesn't exist is unknowable and only believed in. You know what exists, but can only believe in what doesn't.

The significance is, it either exists or it does not, exposing that the misuse of believing occurs when the belief is about nothing at all and is pure fantasy—the belief is there but the thing believed in is not. If the thing believed in truly is there, then this isn't and can't be a belief but a recognisable fact. Once this misuse of belief is clearly exposed, it is then in its proper place as fantasy. Recognised as fantasy it is no longer believed so no longer has an effect and therefore it is no longer harmful. All that remains is the correct use of belief.

UNCOVERING THE HARMFUL EFFECT OF BELIEFS

Belief's real purpose is only to assist our mechanical navigation through life. No harm comes of this. Harm inevitably comes from the misuse of any natural function because the misuse renders the function unnatural and therefore harmful.

Distortion of a function's *use* leads to the redefinition or changing of its *meaning and purpose*. When we redefine meaning and purpose in this way, we cross the line between reality and fantasy and become delusional. Thereby we create confusion around otherwise very straight-forward self-evident facts.

Consider this example. Because people use eating as a way to indulge, soothe themselves, escape feelings of emptiness or numb fear, or for the pleasure of taste alone, a disconnection develops between the sensation of hunger and need for sustenance felt in the body, and the false ideas and reasons for eating.

Similarly when we use belief unnaturally—for indulging in a fantasy or in avoidance of or escape from reality—we cross the line and move from healthy reality into harmful delusions and soon, we cannot define reality from imagination. This is actually both an age-old and current problem of massive proportion which our species has continued to indulge in and decline from.

DISCOVER YOURSELF WITHOUT BELIEFS

The way you can detect and then define reality from illusions caused by belief is that reality can cause no harm or imbalance, whilst belief distorts reality and so causes both.

To expose any unintentional or habitual misuse of belief in your life, check for any ongoing effects of harmful or distressful thoughts about yourself. The most harmful effects come from defining or identifying yourself with a belief. Belief's distortion of your view and understanding of yourself or the real world will be why there is conflict, harm or imbalance in your life. Belief is also responsible for any confusion between what you really can know and what you only imagine and then believe.

To detect the influence of underlying beliefs, watch out for belief's effects in your life. Look for any ongoing conflict or confusion in your life. Notice any habitual words or actions that you regularly use that judge, condemn or undermine you or others. Then if you trace any of those thoughts, words or actions back to their origin inside you, or to what you have believed from others, you will discover that belief is responsible for the pain and ongoing conflict, confusion or harm in your life.

The root cause of all this trouble will be either the known or unknown misuse of belief, but this can be very subtle and hard to detect at first. The effects of harm or distress or conflict in your life are easier to detect, so you can start there.

Honestly consider, take an interest in and try to see how you redefine yourself and your views and distort your life experience with the imaginings of casual or deeply embedded beliefs that you never even realised you had.

Seeing how these beliefs are a distortion of your view and understanding of yourself and of the real world, you can now begin to bring an end to all the pain you have been causing yourself and others through this misunderstood misuse of belief.

It will help you to understand that such beliefs and a need to *believe in something* is simply this—a symptom arising out of a *lost sense of yourself,* and an attempt to both artificially replace that lost sense and fill the need caused by the emptiness of belief. Therefore, due to the artificial nature of beliefs, applying more belief to yourself, whether positive or negative, can only perpetuate that loss. This is because belief is not *you,* it is at best only vaguely *about you* and can only separate you further from the real and fulfilling sense of you. The only cure is reality. Your own real and direct sense of yourself and life as it is without the interpretations of misused beliefs and the divisions and confusions they cause.

The bigger effect from taking on this information on beliefs is you'll realise and break free of beliefs many holds on you and then discover your own true live sense of yourself in the body without them. The following active meditations are designed to help you do this for yourself. They are a way to take all this in, deeper than just thinking about it, into your own feeling of its relevance to you and your life.

Now that you have a clearer understanding of beliefs we can look into judgement. Judgement is the cause of self-dislike and makes it hard for you to experience yourself and life as it really is. Learn how your misuse of judgement prevents change and keeps you stuck in conflict with whatever you judge. That's the topic of the next chapter.

Go to the Active Meditations for this chapter in the Undo app.

PONDER YOUR PROGRESS

What have you noticed since dropping some of your beliefs?

In what way has this understanding changed the way you see yourself or the world in general?

Feel free to note any changes that you can see in yourself... subtle changes are often the deepest changes. The deepest changes are often unknown to us at the time of change and are instead only known to us as the improvements in our physical condition and the reduction of our disturbances with real life situations. So take some time out to ponder that.

NOTES:

_____

_____

_____

_____

_____

_____

_____

_____

_____

_____

CHAPTER SEVEN
JUDGEMENT

Previously you learned that beliefs have a correct and intended mechanical purpose but when they are made up of personal bias or used to redefine ourselves or the factual world, they cause us confusion and suffering.

Today you will be learning how to use judgement intelligently rather than in a way that blocks your intelligence, distorts your perception of reality and causes distress where there is no need for it.

Judgement causes self-dislike. It prevents you from experiencing yourself as you really are. If you don't experience yourself as you really are, how do you *know* you don't like you? You don't!!

CHECK IN WITH YOURSELF

Do you know what judgement is really for?

Where it is harmful and where it is helpful?

Note your answers and then put them aside whilst you complete this chapter. At the end there will be a review of these questions to highlight your progress and help you realise the changes that have naturally happened within you in this process.

DISCOVERING HOW TO LIKE YOURSELF

If you find anything about yourself disturbing or if you think you don't like an aspect of yourself, there is more to this than you may have considered.

Your judgement or criticism of any sensation or aspect of yourself changes your experience of it from how you and any sensations you feel actually *are*, to how you and any sensations then *seem*, when tainted by your judgemental opinions or beliefs.

Dislike of ourselves is always premature to actually knowing ourselves as we are and therefore dislike of ourselves is unreliable, even delusional, and not to be trusted or taken seriously.

Only once judgement and belief about yourself are absent are you in any position to experience you *as you really are* and actually know whether you like or dislike any aspect of yourself. Up until this point, even though you have not known *yourself as you truly are*, you continue to prematurely judge and assume your dislike of one or another aspect of yourself. This mistaken assumption is how we cause an undermining misery in ourselves, maintaining our self-dislike and prevent change.

For any feelings or sensations of self-dislike in you to end, and to enable change, you need to realise that the ideas you have of yourself are not actually *you*. By identifying how these ideas make you feel or think about yourself, and then without further analysis, feeling the physical sensations or tension of that in your body, you will enable the sensations themselves and their effect on you to come to an end in a natural and thorough way.

ACCEPTING OTHERS AS THEY ARE

Judgement and criticism of *others* tends to fall away once a fuller picture of their circumstances or the effects of their life is known to you. It is also helpful when you notice and realise that any felt disturbance you have towards them actually begins within yourself. Recognising and feeling the physical stress of that disturbance in your body will resolve it within you, allowing you to consider others without your disturbance restricting your view of them. It is this deeper understanding of *your* own feelings in yourself that are disturbing you, combined with more complete knowledge of others' circumstances, that takes you beyond your judgement and dislike of them, and enables you to feel at ease with them and to accept them for what they are.

Judgements based on our beliefs and biases do not change the fact of a person or what they are, they only change and falsify our perception of them. The facts of your own or another's characteristic are just that, self-evident neutral facts. They are neither good nor bad, wrong nor right, and are only ever made to appear so through belief, judgement or comparison.

CORRECTING YOUR USE OF JUDGEMENT

Only when we apply our judgement to the mechanical situations in life does it work. It works here because this is its correct and intended use. This correct use of judgement is something we do regularly. When driving, we judge distance for applying our brakes. We all use the practical factual information at hand, not beliefs or biases, to make judgements and navigate our way through various situations all day long. And it works because this is exactly what the thought process of judgement is for. This is its actual and correct use and function.

Imagine the disaster that would eventuate from driving without using fact-based judgements. Imagine relying on bias or personal preferences and beliefs to make our judgements or decisions when driving. It just wouldn't work. It doesn't work in the rest of life either, and the difference you bring to your life once you drop this misuse of judgement is... life works. When you learn to navigate life by impersonal facts alone, it works.

Once we find ourselves no longer blinded by beliefs and biases, the ideas of good and bad, our harsh judgements of ourselves and others give way to a deeper understanding of one another, based in reality itself. Then, no longer divided by ideas, we are receptive to a more commonly shared sense of the facts of life. Recognising that we are all affected and guided by the same facts of life, we find our common ground in life as it really is for all of us. This reveals how fundamentally alike we are, making us more acceptable to one another, easier to understand and live with, and life then becomes far more straight forward.

RESETTING YOUR USE OF JUDGEMENT

It is a mistake to apply the thought process of judgement to our own or another's character or behaviours. That use of judgement results in criticism, condemnation, biased conclusions, and ultimately ignorance of the true and actual nature of the characteristic or person being judged. Therefore when we judge our own or another's character, we are inevitably mistaken.

This misuse of judgement, of a person or their character, our own or another's, is not based on the facts as they are but is based on the thoughts we impose on those facts. These thoughts are simply ideals, opinions, beliefs, learned or cultural biases which we use to create comparisons between how a person, or their character actually *is* and how they or we should *be*, according to those beliefs or ideas. It is this comparison that is responsible for our dissatisfaction with ourselves as we are or others as they are.

The solution comes from understanding the fact or truth of how we already are. This truth is only derived from us being ourselves, rather than trying to be someone or something else, and gaining our self-understanding from that. This also then increases our sense of empathy and understanding for others, which makes it easier for us to allow others to be themselves without us imposing our personal preferences or judgements onto them.

LEARN HOW FACTS FREE US

Clearly, how we *think* a person or character should be or could be is not the way they are. Whatever we *think* is a made-up fiction and whatever they *actually are* is the fact and truth of them. Whether we like it or not, it is the truth.

Even the way we *think* one should be changes with varying cultural beliefs or personal preferences. So it is never a correct understanding. Understanding yourself or another requires a raw un-biased intelligence to see and accept the factual truth of ourselves and others as it is.

Even when the truth is uncomfortable, is it the truth that needs to change or us? To develop or mature, we may have to face up to facts about ourselves or life that at first, we may not want to. Rather than judging these facts of us or ourselves, we can process and resolve our personal restrictions by acting on them as little as possible whilst simply feeling the driving force of their disturbance within us, until it comes to an end. With this new approach, you will emerge from this process more capable and more at ease with the facts of life as they really are.

CLARIFYING THE TWO USES OF JUDGEMENT

Once we are conditioned to believe in cultural, religious or even legal opinions, they become important and personal to us. Then forming our personal views from them, these opinions inevitably become our own thoughts and judgements about others or life outside of us. We then project these views outwardly and can no longer see or accept others or the world as they are. In this way we impose our personal views onto others, which is a misuse of judgement that separates us from them.

And what we usually overlook is the detrimental effects this has on us. When our imagined view of how life or others should be doesn't match with the way they actually are, we cause ourselves unnecessary distress and conflict with how life actually is, and make ourselves disturbed. Then out of our own confusion and disturbance, we blame the people or things we have judged for causing our self-induced disturbances and feel justified for judging or criticising them, which only disturbs us even more.

And so, because we project our own learned, imagined and personalised views onto the facts of life, we thereby mis-interpret those facts and cause our own disturbances. In this way we prevent ourselves from receiving and understanding the raw facts from life outside us, as they really are, and create our own ignorance to life as it is.

Without the interference of our imagined views, we are otherwise sensitively equipped and able to receive the raw facts from life outside of us onto the blank canvas of our sensory receptors, and we can therefore understand life as it really is. Without fixed or biased views with which to com-pare life's facts, we have no reason to judge and dislike life or ourselves or others at all, and no way to cause ourselves distress over the way these are.

If we are to avoid the harmful misuse of judgement, it is important to understand that judgement is only for making mechanical decisions in life and that judgement relies on and must be based on the facts we receive from life to work. These essential facts are already there to be known from life, but once we add our personal preferences, we distort the facts and prevent this factual information from life ever reaching us. Essentially it is through this misuse of judgement, that we perpetuate our own ignorance of whatever we judge.

A characteristic or person is quite separate from your thoughts or judgements about them. The influence of these thoughts about yourself or others in fact blinds you to the person or characteristics as they really are.

Having this mistaken application of judgement revealed to you here, if you are ever to know yourself as you really are or know another as they really are you need to understand the difference between the two uses of judgement. So take your time to absorb and understand this and you will then be more able to live in relative ease with yourself and others, however these are.

The next chapter is solely on Maturing your Meditation. It will identify and clarify any myths you may have heard about meditation and the mind, as well as what to pay attention to and what to ignore to help you sink into the deeper meditation of your body, naturally.

The more you meditate this way, the more experiential your understanding will become. And the deeper your experiential understanding becomes, the deeper, easier and more natural your meditation will be for you. The next chapter is especially focussed on what meditation is and what it isn't, to prepare you for the most interesting and liberating parts to follow.

Go to the Active Meditations for this chapter in the Undo app.

PONDER YOUR PROGRESS

Has there been any change in your motivation level?

Did you know there is a significant difference between the harmless mechanical judgements for navigating life and the harmful judgement of yourself or others that lead to criticism, condemnation, conflict and distress?

Did you set out to change these things or did they just happen on their own, simply from hearing this information and getting involved in this chapter?

Feel free to note any changes that you can see in yourself... subtle changes are often the deepest changes. The deepest changes are often unknown to us at the time of change and are instead only known to us as the improvements in our physical condition and the reduction of our disturbances with real life situations. So take some time out to ponder that.

NOTES:

_____

_____

_____

_____

_____

_____

_____

_____

_____

_____

_____

CHAPTER EIGHT
MATURING YOUR MEDITATION

So far we have been developing and building the essential understanding of various aspects of your human nature to enable you to meditate naturally.

Your deeper understanding and the discoveries achieved to this point are shaping your foundation for a meditative life when you are active and for deep meditation when you're still. You are developing a more permanent natural condition of meditation from the inside out—rather than creating a short-lived meditation experience from the outside in.

Today you will be learning about the correct and incorrect approaches to yourself when meditating, how the way and what we have learned to think have caused confusion, and how natural meditation can free you from these effects. This will help you mature in your meditation and save you from unnecessary difficulties. As your understanding grows, so your meditation will strengthen and deepen, becoming an ever-increasing support in your life.

Meditation is *not* a luxury, it's an absolute necessity. The way you feel and think is the foundation of action and living.

The quality of these determines the quality and potential of every other part of your life. If you know how to and do take care of this foundational aspect of you, you will easily recover from the effects of life each day and be ready to face life afresh the next day.

CHECK IN WITH YOURSELF

Did you know that you don't need to change the way you are?

Did you know that only when your bias and judgement changes, can you understand and be fulfilled with how and what you already are?

What problems do you think meditation can help solve?

Note your answers and then put them aside whilst you complete this chapter. At the end there will be a review of these questions to highlight your progress and help you realise the changes that have naturally happened within you in this process.

RECOVERING FROM THE DAILY EFFECTS OF LIFE

Living out each day of your life has many effects on you. There are the obvious needs such as food, rest, finances and relationships—all of which you are aware of. But what you may not be as aware of is that whenever you override distress or ignore your daily feelings, you actually neglect your most basic needs. This causes tensions in the body, which accumulate and increase each time you neglect yourself.

As these tensions accumulate, they change your health, the way your body functions, how it feels to be you, and how you then think and act. They even change your age, not in time but in your overall condition. That we are affected in many ways in a single day of life is obvious and experienced by everyone.

Without meditation, most people are otherwise poorly equipped to either recognise or recover from the effects of this underlying level of self-neglect. If you don't meditate, your quality of life will be massively reduced by comparison to what it can be with meditation, and your need to recover from the effects of life is neglected. Then over time, the build-up of the effects from these tensions throughout your body will lead to the acceleration of your overall decline.

This is why real meditation is *not* a luxury, it is an absolute necessity, perhaps even a greater necessity than quality food and sleep. If the way you feel and think is unhealthy, you will struggle in every aspect of your life. Whereas if you know how to take care of these most basic and foundational needs and do so, you will easily recover from the effects of life each day and be ready to face life afresh the next day. Because the way you feel and think is the foundation of action and living, the quality of these within you determines the quality and potential of every other part of your life. So take the time to meditate daily, and see how the overall quality of your life improves.

ANCHORING YOURSELF IN REALITY

There are a few misconceptions around meditation and the first one is that meditation is about the mind.

The foundation and depth of natural meditation is in physical sensation, which exists before any thinking occurs. When you are sensing, and only through sensing, are you able to experience yourself as you are and all life in connection with you as it actually is.

When you're thinking, you're experiencing the added taint or *effects* of your thinking mixed with whatever you're purely sensing, which can prevent you from experiencing your sense of yourself or the reality of life as it purely and truly is. Thinking can consume your attention and numb out or override your true and primary felt sense of yourself in the body of you and of life outside of you.

When you are distracted and disconnected from your sense of yourself, thinking then has no anchor in reality and becomes meaningless confusion or fantasy. This disconnection is the original cause of self-ignorance and insensitivity and therefore is the origin of what enables all harm in life. This then leads to further confusion, illusions, mistakes and unnecessary difficulties, and eventually brings about mental or physical illness.

To reconnect with reality and truly meditate, you can simply exit this confusing effect of thinking by settling back into the physical felt reality of sensing throughout the body of you. By attuning to the deeper sensations in your body, you leave the shallow confusions and distresses of thinking or imagining behind, to come to their own end in their own time. These deeper bodily sensations are the true silent depths of meditation and this is all experienced within your own body.

The so-called mind or activity of thinking has nothing to do with meditation. In this approach to meditation, you are immersing into the origin of thought, within the physical sensations in the body that drive thinking. Hence by just feeling those sensations, you relieve any urge, distress or need for thinking and burn out the energy that fuels unnecessary thinking. All of this is why, at this sensory depth in the body, thinking is no longer a problem when you are meditating in this way.

When meditating this way, you never have to consider thought at all, unless you have an immediate use or mechanical need for it. Thought is or soon becomes for you a tool that you manifest on demand when needed. Otherwise it is not there. At first, thinking will habitually seem to exist but as you continue with this deeper approach and increase your understanding, thought's appearance will gradually fade and its imagined effects will weaken.

Rather than imposing techniques, understanding is the basis which enables you to meditate deeply. And ironically, this deeper meditation is the origin from which this understanding flows—from the felt sense in and of the body. In fact, sensation both precedes and includes all understanding, which in turn precedes all thought and action used to express ourselves in life. Which is why only the natural meditation of the body will attune you to this massive source of sensory intelligence that is necessary for ease of living.

RESTORING YOUR POWER OVER THOUGHT

When you are meditating, it does not matter that you are thinking. Because the truth is, you only 'think you are thinking'. You forget that thought is only imagined by you and therefore has no real power over you because it is not actually there. It doesn't really exist but only appears to by your ability to imagine it. Certainly, for now it seems real and really there to you, and therefore seems to have power. This is due to you forgetting or not yet understanding how the body produces thought. So you forget that you are its maker and that only its *seeming* to be real gives it imagined power. This is the characteristic of imagination or illusion. It appears to exist but does not.

It is only due to our overuse of thought and overthinking that we make thought an unnatural constant activity, which is why we rarely live from our natural quiet depths of sensing. In this natural quiet of yourself in the body and in the prolonged absence of thought's activity, thought is revealed to be nothing in its own right, just an on-off function, which you—the body—conjures up and puts to use when required.

We have all given too much significance and importance to our thinking, given thought too prominent a role in our lives, a role which you are now discovering is more effectively taken care of via purely sensing. Your over concern with or valuing of the *contents* of your thoughts is the main interest and confusion drawing you in. This *interest in the content of your thoughts keeps you thinking* and causes you to give power to something which isn't really there, other than in you imagining or believing it to be.

ATTUNING YOURSELF TO THE SOLUTIONS OF LIFE

By familiarising yourself with the deeper *felt* sensations in your body and *not* concerning yourself with the contents of your thinking, you will come to recognise two very significant truths; that thoughts are only superficial descriptions or imaginings, and that thoughts, words and images are caused by these deeper bodily sensations. You will come to see that words and images are all essentially thoughts and how all these forms of thought are just the final fragmented expressions of the greater source of information held in and originating from these bodily sensations.

As you discover and realise that the contents of your thinking originates in the sensations within you, you will also realise that sensations both precede and are actually the cause of thought. From this, you will ultimately realise that you have nothing more to gain from thought's second-hand content. For you already have the untainted, complete and original sense of it within you.

Realising this connection and yet difference between thoughts and sensations, you no longer crave for or worry over what you imagine you may miss out on because you realise you already sense it within you. Once free of this imagined concern, you are not so drawn to thinking, you are released from paying unnecessary attention to thought and so you naturally gravitate back into the source of sensory information and knowing within your body. Then and there, you find you are both quiet and fully informed, and no longer drawn to the secondary content and stories of thinking.

To meditate and gain your deeper sense of self and understanding of all things, let thinking go on unattended without concern for it, whilst you notice and feel the continual and deeper physical sensations throughout the body of you. Your *felt* sense of whatever you feel in the flesh of the body of you is your source of deepest meditation, which will re-sensitise and strengthen automatically, and also heal you of the effects of life as you feel them.

FEELING YOUR TOTAL INTERCONNECTEDNESS

When you are meditating, it is important that you only concern yourself with what you physically sense and no more, nothing extra. Don't try to change, improve or achieve anything.

Sensations of the body are the primary reality of being you and the only way to actually know you or even know you exist. Thought cannot do either of these. This sense of *'all it is to be you'* is the essence and foundation of everything natural meditation is.

Relying on the naturalness of sensing to guide, inform and activate any healing within you is what makes this meditation so direct and effective. As your understanding and personal experience of this expands, your meditation will mature and you will discover the self-evident and obvious, yet enormous, effects of natural meditation in your life for yourself.

Although the live sensations within and beneath your own skin are all you need for knowing yourself, to know the world outside and beyond your own skin requires you to use your senses. Through thinking, we interpret and distort what we sense but from the deeper sensory reality of ourselves in the body and without thought's interpretation, we are fully able to receive and understand life outside us, exactly as it is.

This sensory connection to life is literally an outward extension of your sense of self, connecting you with the world outside you. This is the natural way to live a meditative life, just as all animals live in meditative, sensory connection with life.

Therefore the only additions you need to your own live physical sense of yourself are your senses—eyes, ears and so on and the *felt* touch of your skin. These are your essential connection to the world. Again, whilst you *only* hear a sound, view a sight or feel a touch, you have these primary physical live sensations connecting you to the world around you. Once you add thoughts as a description or perception to what your senses receive—what your eyes see, your ears hear or your skin feels—you create and superimpose the numbing effects of thought about what your senses are receiving.

This distracts you from the pure sense of wisdom only known through the primary live sense of these organs. The secondary mechanical activity of describing your perceptions or ideas about what you sense actually numbs you to them. This is how you lose touch with the fullness of the actual sensations of life and the living, and with the purity of whatever your senses receive.

Through thought's interpretation, you lose your true and perfectly acceptable connection to life and your deeper felt understanding of everything outside you. Just notice how you lose the sense fulfilment of sitting in a hot bath of water whenever you drift off into the activity of thinking.

Natural meditation is simply being engaged in life fully and as it truly is. When you are sensorily connected in yourself and sensorily receptive to life outside, you are able to enjoy and benefit from your primary *sense* activity in a natural way.

The whole physical sense of you and in you is all there is to this meditation. Other than this, there is only what you imagine or think about. This physical sense of you is as deep and still and rejuvenating as it gets. Yet as it is of the body of you, it is also alive and dynamic, free of the fixed restrictions and the superficiality of traditions, or your own personal bias or ideas.

Now I will share some rare tips from my life experience of meditating naturally. They will help you to remain anchored in your own quiet sense of yourself in the body, rather than being drawn into overthinking, reacting to pain or avoiding meditation.

THE BENEFITS OF SITTING STILL... Just staying physically still is enough. Physical stillness is your anchor. Being physically still will always attune you to feeling the sensations deeper within you. From this you will begin to notice that just being in the live sensory existence of you in the body, you gradually detect all the differences and subtleties of the sensations in the body—or of being you. If you sit still for long enough and do nothing more, healing within your system will naturally activate. Wherever you have been stuck or held back will begin to release. Suppressed or known pain or distress will activate to heal you from within. Your thinking will become clearer and your physical health will rejuvenate. All this will happen as long as you don't do anything else other than sit physically still.

RESISTANCE TO PAIN CAUSES YOU TO SUFFER PAIN... Understanding the significance of pain allows you to feel and process it without resisting or suffering your pain or distress as it heals during meditation. You will have discomfort at times but through understanding how to process any resistance or reaction to pain, you will then truly feel any pain as it is without these amplified distortions, and then you won't suffer from it, you'll be relieved to feel it.

WHY YOU AVOID MEDITATION… There is a deeper, even sneaky, reason why you put off or avoid meditating. Just beneath the surface of what you are fully aware of within yourself lies unresolved pain or disturbances. The underlying feeling of these cause unconscious habitual resistance to feeling them and so you avoid meditating because of them. Understanding this and remembering to be honest about this whenever you find any little reason to put off meditating is part of maturing as a meditator. Seeing that meditation is exactly what you need, more than ever at these times, and knowing how meditating will take care of these disturbances, you will be more responsive to taking care of your needs by sitting through the smaller purgings of these from within you, whenever they occur.

THERE IS NOTHING TO GAIN… There is nothing to gain from the contents of your thinking when you are meditating. When meditating, your thinking is mostly forming out of all the obsolete and old memories and distresses held, and now purging from within your body. And so, you have nothing to gain from this type of thinking. You have nothing more to learn from it. You have lived with the feelings and the influence of these for a long time, and now, when you are meditating, this old information is activating and purging from these deeper sensations and simply forming the content of your current thinking now, as you meditate. Understanding this, the deeper sensations of your body become your primary interest and you realise that they are all you need when meditating.

THERE IS NOTHING TO ACHIEVE… Truly understanding that there is nothing to achieve and no way to improve on what you really are. This leaves you free of any urge or goal to achieve or want more than what you are when meditating. Because both wanting and striving are the main reason you continue thinking and remain shallow during meditation, understanding this enables you to sink beneath all your thinking, to let thinking fade away and to appreciate and realise the deeper significance of yourself however you are.

THERE IS NO MIND… Understanding that thought or the mind does not exist in its own right, it is simply a mechanical function. This enables you to sit quietly for prolonged periods in the depths of the existing sensations of all that you are without your thinking becoming a problem. The false idea of a permanent thinker we have called the mind gives thinking an existence equal to an organ, which it doesn't really have. Realising both thinking and thought to be one and the same, mere images the body conjures out of a mix of chemistry and deeper physical sensations, you realise thinking is only imagined. You only *think you are thinking* when in fact nothing is there, and so you are blank. Mind or thought is neither there nor real, and so, based in this reality, this realisation, how can it be a problem when you are meditating? It can't be and it isn't.

These are the tips that will really make a difference to your meditation… and now you can experience and explore these tips as part of the Active Meditations.

You will have really progressed a long way in this chapter, but we're going to keep going. Next we have the chapter on Bodymind, to help you reconnect and remove the separation between your body and thinking. Then you'll have even more stability and clarity in the feelings and thoughts that arise from inside of you.

Go to the Active Meditations for this chapter in the Undo app.

PONDER YOUR PROGRESS

Having completed this chapter on meditation, what things inside of yourself do you now think meditation can help solve?

Feel free to note any changes that you can see in yourself… subtle changes are often the deepest changes. The deepest changes are often unknown to us at the time of change and are instead only known to us as the improvements in our physical condition and the reduction of our disturbances with real life situations. So take some time out to ponder that.

NOTES:

_____

_____

_____

_____

_____

_____

_____

_____

_____

_____

_____

CHAPTER NINE
BODYMIND

In this chapter you'll begin to understand the significance of reconnecting the disconnection between your body and what you have been taught to think of as your mind. You'll start to see more clearly that all thinking originates as the tensions or stresses and a variety of sensations or feelings in your body. That it's all a part of one continuous, alive physical function starting very simply as a physical sensation in a particular part of your body that continues through to more specific feelings, and then continues further, out into your various external or outer expressions in life as your thoughts, words and actions.

To divide the focus and awareness of yourself into separate parts, such as a mind and body, and to make yourself oblivious to the existence of any one of these parts of you is a fundamental problem, and is the root and cause of all other problems in the human world. In this chapter, I will help you see even more clearly that there are not two of you—a mind and a body—but that the function we call mind is an integral part of the one and only body of you. The more this becomes clear to you, the more you will naturally listen to, sense, know and operate from all of you at once. This is what allows you to remain connected and in continual self-understanding and good health until the day you die.

CHECK IN WITH YOURSELF

Are you aware of any relationship between the way you are feeling, your moods, your thinking and the sensations within the different parts of your body?

Have you ever noticed that stimulations of different parts of your body coincide with what you feel, think, and desire?

Note your answers and then put them aside whilst you complete this chapter. At the end, there will be a review of these questions to highlight your progress and help you realise the changes that have naturally happened within you in this process.

MY EARLY INSIGHTS INTO THE BODY-MIND CONNECTION

There were three main stages in my early discoveries of the mind being an embodied and physical function. During my teen years, in the 1970's, I became interested in body language for reading and understanding people when I was interacting with them. At that early stage of my development, it was only the postures and gestures that I was drawn to and found helpful in life. And for a young guy growing towards adulthood, without me fully realising it, this gave me an edge in relating to people in both personal relationships and in my work life. Even this comparatively tiny level of insight made my life in these areas far easier. I began to understand that the direct language of the body was always truthful and revealed far more than what people would think and say. Realising the body doesn't lie but only expresses facts, I wanted to know more about this.

Body language is our communication through gestures and postures. Even if we try to hide our true feelings or intentions from others or our true condition from ourselves, they, including our attempts to hide them, are revealed through the unspoken language of our bodies. The pattern of expression generated from our physical sensations and true feelings is maintained through every posture and gesture, every function, and also every condition of our health we find ourselves in. These revealing patterns of expression are automatic and inescapable. Every living creature comes into expression and performs action from this primary driving force of bodily instinct or feelings. Action is the manifestation of this. Think about it... is any action performed without some reason or degree of purpose or intention?

Whether you want it to be or not, your reason or intention is conveyed through your body language of the way you hold yourself, your physical condition at the time, and even your odour. For example, the folding of our arms when we are being spoken to may indicate resistance to the person speaking or the words spoken. Rounding the shoulders indicates carrying an overload of burden or an exaggerated sense of responsibility. Or sometimes, it indicates poor self-esteem or cowering. Fear is easily sensed by animals or sensitive humans. Even plants have a sensed response to our intentions. Nowadays body language is more commonly known. It is a simple example of the mind embodied and all forms of expression, originating in the body.

UNDERSTANDING THE NATURAL INTEGRATION PROCESS

The second and main stage of my discoveries was in my early twenties, when I was about three years into my life as a monk. I developed a twisted pelvis and severe back pain, which continued until I started listening to all that these conditions had to reveal about my situation. Unknown to me at the time, this was my body naturally opposing the direction my life was taking. Also unknown to me, my daily self-imposing of dogmatic ideals and meditations of the monk was dissociating me further and further from my true and natural self, and my body was saving me from this self-destruction. Over my remaining four years as a monk, the natural process of the body revealed itself.

For a monk, meditation always involves the belief in a mind and the use of thinking to aspire to an imagined purer, holy state of self-imposed, artificially constructed idealism. However, in contrast to this, I was acutely conscious of my physicality—and throughout the body of me something was changing on its own.

A part of what was occurring for me during prolonged periods of physical stillness (what I later realised as the natural meditation of the body) was all sorts of sensations, including physical pain or even the sensations present during illness, when illness was there. These sensations became all that I was aware of when meditating, without any thoughts, descriptions, reactions to or analysis of these. I continued to feel these sensations of pain or distress or illness when they occurred, and eventually they would dissipate and heal in their own time. During and following the dissipation and out-flowing of those bodily sensations, my forgotten memories of unresolved experiences gathered throughout my life returned.

Fortunately, this release also included the effects of my more recent indoctrination from being a monk, as a variety of memories sprang to life as the pain dissipated during these meditations. Some memories were petty and seemingly unimportant while other memories flowed forth with events and old distresses, pains or influences of my past that had detrimentally affected and changed me. Most importantly, what always followed, for no reason known to me at the time and from no intention or effort on my part, was that troublesome characteristics, both physical and mental or habitual, would leave me and never return.

So completely resolved were these that I would often only later notice their absence, and only notice them because they were no longer playing out or no longer present in situations that had previously triggered them. I simply found myself changed with no intention to change myself. My body—nature—was correcting itself and returning to its natural original state.

CONFIRMING THE BODYMIND DISCOVERY

The third stage of discovery reconfirmed my previous personal discoveries of the bodymind connection, that the mind was embodied, and that this understanding was equally as relevant to others and their healing as to me and my own. Up until this point, its relevance to others hadn't occurred to me or yet been confirmed. Nor had it occurred to me that I had discovered a universal truth required for complete natural healing. From this point forward I began developing ways to bring this understanding to others.

After being ousted from the community of monks and nuns, I reintroduced myself into the real world. I opened a healing and meditation clinic which was an overnight success. From the start, whenever I massaged the deeper stress or pain held in the same body part of different patients, such as their shoulder, hip or knee, they expressed and revealed the same concerns about themselves or their lives. This occurred with literally hundreds of people.

With hundreds of people consistently expressing exactly the same topics of concern when the same part of their body was massaged, this repeatedly showed me the common link between the mental state or deeper feeling being expressed and the corresponding and aligning body part being stimulated by the deep massage.

What was also revealed and very significant, was that the action performed or function of the particular body part on which I was working aligned with the nature of the complaint, distress or concern in their life, which they were expressing when contacting and feeling the pain in that part.

What I had discovered was that, within the physical pain in any one spot in the human body lay the specific unresolved memory harbouring the concerns or traumas of that person. Another aspect also revealed in this was that pain and corresponding ailments manifested in that spot for reasons relating to the action, expression and purpose of that muscle, organ or limb in the person's life. By treating these as one integral problem, the patient was able to achieve full recovery, and achieve this relatively easily.

LEARNING ABOUT YOUR UNIQUE EXPRESSION

Each part of our body has a very specific physical function, specific action and expression. Each part can only be driven into action by related feelings, thoughts, desires and intentions, which in turn can only come into expression through the actions that only those specific body parts are capable of. Only through that particular action can whatever we are feeling and thinking and so desiring to express, come into action.

For example, try not breathing for a while and you will soon feel a powerful urge to breath. That urge is the power driving that action. But even then, if your lungs are clogged up with feelings of grief, sadness, loss or sorrow, your interest in life or even your will to live fully can dwindle, and the force of that corresponding urge lessens. And hence your breathing is inhibited.

You may begin to breathe more shallowly to avoid stirring those deeper feelings within your lungs. Or you may even inhale smoke to suppress stimulation of the distress in there. Because of the distress held in your lungs, you feel less like using your lungs to their full extent and may become less interested in the more active parts of life. Feeling less vital, stifled or emotionally withheld, you only want minimal engagement in life while you feel that way. But as the feelings in your lungs heal and return to normal, you find yourself breathing more deeply or engaging in life in more vigorous ways again, and taking life in more fully again.

Consider another example. You have a voice with which to express yourself. But even when you have something to say, if you feel too frightened to speak up, to express or reveal yourself, it becomes difficult for you to find the words, or your throat closes over or tightens up, develops a cough to inhibit your speech, or in some way, your words are held back. Only by processing those fears will you find the full use of that body part and the expression of yourself it can enable.

Even if you don't perform the desired action or expression, the corresponding desire or feeling driving it is still felt in the body part for a while until it is fully absorbed back into the body from where it came. In the same way, when pain holds you back from action, feeling that pain will trigger its recovery, and as the pain or feeling corresponding to the action of that body part resolves, you will regain more and more freedom and the fuller use and expression of that part again. That part will then return to its strong and healthy state.

LEARNING TO FUNCTION AS ONE

No condition or action of the body exists in isolation to the feelings and thoughts generated in each part. There are always co-existing and relating feelings, thoughts, desires, memories, pain or intentions driving every action or held within every condition. Therefore there is no way to separate or divide our daily actions, expressions and conditions into solely a physical condition and solely a mental condition. They are always together as one, and as one, comprise everything that makes up our entire being, and it is this totality that drives every expression or action in life.

At no point in our existence do any of us experience any-thing else but that. Not even when we try to escape the real effects of our life experiences on any part of our whole self through imagination, denial or suppression, or try to overcome those effects through force. We are unable to overcome the reality of our condition. If we are physically inhibited, the urges relying on that inhibited body part to express are also inhibited. If we are inhibited by feelings of pain or trauma or the suppression of these, or simply emotionally upset in one area of our life expression, whether we acknowledge these or not, they inhibit the vitality of the physical part we would use to act on that particular urge.

For example, if you are physically impotent, you may want to have sex, but you are also overpowered by deeper yet opposing feelings or ideas that mess up your chemistry, affect your vitality and inhibit or prevent that body part from functioning.

So you see, everything that makes up the whole of what we are is always functioning together and as one. And the condition of any one part of our body has a coexisting feeling, pain, trauma or way of thinking contributing to the condition and performance of that body part. Never do we truly experience one part of ourselves without the other. We have only learned to intellectually refer to our one whole self-expression as though it is two separate unrelated functions.

Our oblivion to parts of our existence doesn't change the fact of what we are and the way we function. That is, we are one body with many functions. We are not one specific function, a mind or a soul living off the other part, being the body. In fact, no one function can exist without being part of the whole body. Separated from the whole body and without the life of the body to keep it alive, separated parts simply die. Even our blood and urine is alive with cells and proteins and all the live parts that make up life, but once separated from the whole, once it leaves our body, all those living cells eventually die.

Whatever we think or say or do also affects the way we feel in our body. However we feel in our body determines our experience of life. It is present in the way we think and feel about our life, and also present in the tone of our voice and in the quality of our actions. The condition of the way we feel drives and becomes behaviours, both harmful and helpful. The following will help you resolve the harmful and be supported by the helpful guidance from within you.

LIVING AS A CONNECTED PERSON

The way we can know why we do what we do and why we live the life we choose to live is for us to feel and know where we are coming from in our bodies, to know what those feelings are telling us, and what quality of urge is driving us from within.

Knowing this whole picture of ourselves as we operate, starting from the simple sensations we feel through to more specific feelings, thoughts, words and actions that form our outer life, we can determine our lives according to what is harmful or what is healthy and true to us. We can choose to feel any destructive urges to their end inside us, rather than acting on them and bringing the harm out into our lives and the lives of others. We can also feel when the urge or feeling is right for us and so be confident in what we choose to do in life.

Otherwise, when there is a disconnection between body and mind, or between what we feel and think and do, we are oblivious to where we are coming from and live our lives blindly. Which means that we live our lives misguided, unknowingly following urges originating in unresolved pain inside of us, or ideas others have influenced us to think throughout our lives, and we live driven by the confusion within ourselves.

Because we don't understand the equal significance of each stage of our whole function, and how it progresses from physical sensations to feelings then thoughts, and then the actions that express these, we ignore and underestimate, or mistrust and misunderstand, the deeper subtle guidance of our feelings. We then over-rely on thinking to get us through life. But thinking is such a minimal part of this entire function and on its own is not enough. When we no longer know what our feelings are telling us, we live disconnected and confused when we don't have to be.

Living as whole and connected person simply means being sensitive to ourselves from the physical sensations within our body through to the expression of these as our thoughts, words and actions in life. Living this way connects us with our deeper humanness and our much-needed natural intelligence for life, out of which we are unable to do harm. When you can appreciate the significance of this, you realise it is really the ultimate solution to all our problems.

LEARNING TO LISTEN TO YOURSELF

To develop your natural ability for knowing what your feelings are telling you, you can begin by noticing how feelings are either slightly different or more obviously different in each body part; that they are specific to each body part and its action. Then soon, you'll begin to see that the action each feeling urges you to do is also completely different.

You can easily interpret and understand feelings of hunger for example, and you know you only feel those in your stomach. You know what those feelings are telling you to do. And then once you have eaten enough, the feelings in your stomach change from hunger to satiation and tell you that you've had enough.

You are also familiar with sexual feelings and exactly where they originate in your body. You know what they drive you to do or want to do.

Feelings of disturbance are also felt in specific parts of your body and have their own feel to them. They contain their own unique information specific to the action or to the inhibitions and the consequent inaction of that body part, and they also affect how you associate with the action the body part is used for.

Here is a good example. When a person feels indecisive over their future direction, they procrastinate and put things off. They struggle with decision making and avoid dealing with the next step in their lives. As they are not moving forward, over time they feel in a rut, can't think clearly or with confidence and become fearful over the future.

Or when a marriage breaks up, and we are forced into a dramatic disruptive change in direction. This forced disruption brings on an understandable resistance to any future disruptions in your life and to any sudden changes of direction your life will take. This affects both the direction of your life and how you move forward into the next part of it.

All of this type of distress is felt as tensions that mostly build up in the tissue of the pelvis and legs. This is because the function of this area, which is to carry or propel us forward, is frustrated and in conflict. With every step forward, there is hesitation and procrastination holding you back, so the muscles are both pushing forward and pulling back. In time, the pelvis itself commonly twists, causing lower spine curvature, and on it goes.

Then without knowing how you feel inside or where you are coming from and what drives or inhibits you, you do not understand why these physical ailments have occurred. And not knowing how to listen to each part of your body and feel the distress within there, you do not know why you struggle to move forward in life or the real reason for your physical ailments. And importantly, you don't know how to heal either your struggle or your coexisting physical ailment. Consequently, you are literally stuck in a rut.

Whether it is physical pain or feelings of hesitation or fear of life, when these are felt as they are in that area of your body, you will discover that they are both telling you the same thing. In this example, the core essence of what your body is telling you is that you are stuck and distressed over unclear direction in one or another area of your life. And when feeling the sensations of the afflicted areas, you will feel the basic feeling of being stuck. They, the pain of the area and the way you feel starting from inside that area, are simply two expressions of one and the same condition, which you need to feel to process and heal.

It is important not to see this as a mental condition causing a physical condition or a physical condition causing a mental condition. They are essentially one and the same thing. Mind is just another word for body. It is an embodied function. To think is an action of the body and by tuning back into the feelings within you, you will find that all information flows from these.

FINDING ANSWERS FROM YOUR BODY

All thinking originates as the tensions or stresses and a variety of sensations or feelings in the body. By now you will be beginning to understand for yourself that thinking is entirely a physical function. The significance and connection between a part of the body, the sensations felt there, and the fundamental topic of your thinking is quite mechanical and specific. And if you are to benefit from the complete knowledge of yourself and life that is available in this connection, it is important to understand the mechanics of this biological computer that we all are. Now you know how thinking, originating as these physical sensations, initially shows itself in the area or function of the body that most specifically expresses that thinking in action.

Referring back to the example of hunger, how do we know we are hungry? We feel it. Our ability to know we are hungry is determined by the physical sense or *feeling* of hunger. And where do we feel it? In our stomach.

What we feel and where we feel it tells us what we need to know. There is no way we can use thought to know of any condition as that condition is occurring in our body, and so to know we are hungry or to know however we are or whatever our needs are, we must feel it. Thought cannot help us in this. In this we need and use our body's felt sense. In this felt sensation in the stomach, there is a sense of information. A knowing *that* we need food and even *which* food we need.

When needing food, it is through the changes in our chemistry caused by our smell and taste that we can determine and sense our needs more precisely. When we ask ourselves, "What do I *feel like?*", we form the answer from the information felt within all of that sensing and feeling. Even as we reach satiation, the smell and taste of our food changes from pleasurable to less pleasurable to mild repulsion, which tells us that we have had enough, right down to the specifics of a particular type of food. The 'feeling' of hunger goes and we know to stop eating. Again, it is through these physical sensations and *not* through thought that we *know* we have had our fill. If you rely on your thinking alone, you won't know when or what or how much to eat. In fact, when we are disconnected from our bodily sensations and relying solely on thinking, which is only memory and desire, we eat addictively and poorly, and end up with eating disorders and illnesses and even death. So you simply can't rely on thinking for guidance. You absolutely need sensory intelligence for this, and to rely on the live sensations that are informing you from deeper within your body.

Thought can't sense or feel anything. That is not its purpose. Thinking only forms at the tail end of the information process, purely to describe and express in words what we already sense and know in our body.

Another area of this knowing function, of our felt sensed activity in the flesh, also happens when you have just finished a conversation with someone and are left with a feeling of having forgotten to tell them something. You can't *think* what it was that you forgot to say but you feel it there in your body. You probe at that feeling trying to recall what you feel sure you forgot. When you eventually remember, what actually occurs is that the felt information held as tensions in your body releases into expression in the form of your thinking and speech. Finally, once this memory recall from your body occurs, you feel a relief from the felt tension that was telling you that you forgot something. Only once this occurs can you feel fully relieved of that feeling of slight agitation and move on.

Can you see how this physical tension felt in your body is or was the original form and source of the cognitive memory and information you had just recovered and acted on? And how recovering and acting on that information then resolved the original tension?

APPLYING PREVENTATIVE HEALTHCARE IN LIFE

The most crucial areas in which we are reliant on resolving tension is that of our physical and mental health, which are of course paramount to our survival. Health problems are indicators of whatever potential harm we overlook. Pain and illness, to which I have dedicated the next two core chapters, are not there to harm us but are there to prevent us harming ourselves further. They are a crucial information source with the purpose of enabling our self-guidance, self-correction—prevention, and self-recovery.

Health problems result from overlooking or ignoring this same bodily capacity for a deeper *felt sense* of intelligence, which as an alert to harm, initially forms as tensions or distress. If we misread or ignore these tensions, our condition increasingly deteriorates. If we continue to ignore or override these even once illness or pain has developed, they will decline into more extreme illness or pain and eventual death. Pain and illness are informing and protecting us. They are there to ensure our healthy survival, to literally save us from destroying ourselves.

The first basis for *minimising* illness and pain is to not ignore or avoid the initial disturbing feelings in your body but to feel and respond to them. The first basis for then *healing* illness or pain is also to feel the sensations and distresses within it, within you, whilst you are unwell or in pain, without resisting, fighting, or trying to quick-fix it, but to inevitably live within the restrictions and distress it temporarily causes you as you heal.

Whatever the affected part or function of your body prevents you from doing, and whatever frustration or topics of thoughts about yourself that fires up and activates within you, this is revealing the incorrect pattern of thinking to you. It is revealing the suppressed pain behind it and is a part of that entire unwell condition. And it is purging. So don't react to any thoughts, fears or concerns that occur as you are healing. But learn from them. They are often a replay of the type of thinking that caused your illness in the first place.

From these fears and concerns, you can see what has been incorrect in your thinking about yourself or life, and let these burn away with the rest of your illness or pain. Trust your body in this. It is ultimately the only healer of itself. And therefore, as you are the body, you are the ultimate and only healer of yourself.

Your suffering of pain or illness is essentially made up of a combined force of the obvious physical breakdown in one or more areas of your body, your mental reaction, and the specific felt sense of physical distress present in related areas. The area of distress in your body and the activity its function enables you to perform is specifically the area of your life in which you have been acting out behaviours or beliefs that are not healthy or good for you.

When your behaviours or beliefs are at odds with the way you really want to be or need to be, or would be if honest and true to yourself, you will feel a distress somewhere in your body. This distress indicates the conflict with what you are doing and is an alarm for you to cease harming yourself in the course of your life.

This natural function has been ignored, distorted and minimalised in its use due to our over-reliance on thinking, leading us to believing in the fictitious separation between a mind and a body. This oversight has desensitised us to this wealth of essential information and self-guidance for living within us.

Now that I've helped you understand what you may think of as a mind is in fact your body, you'll begin to realise that everything about you is embodied. You can also begin to learn how to end the disconnection from yourself and to truly know yourself as one whole being. As you learn how to reconnect your body and mind, you will begin your journey towards a more fulfilling and content life within yourself, and live a more connected life with the world of which you are part. Up next is the chapter on the Significance of Pain.

Go to the Active Meditations for this chapter in the Undo app.

PONDER YOUR PROGRESS

Are you now more aware of the deeper feelings within you that drive you to think, act and be the way you are and live the life you live?

Feel free to note any changes that you can see in yourself… subtle changes are often the deepest changes. The deepest changes are often unknown to us at the time of change and are instead only known to us as the improvements in our physical condition and the reduction of our disturbances with real life situations. So take some time out to ponder that.

NOTES:

CHAPTER TEN

THE SIGNIFICANCE OF PAIN

In THIS CHAPTER I WILL BE helping you to realise that pain and illness are a crucial source of information for the purpose of self-guidance and self-correction. Pain is poorly understood but it's a really interesting topic. Having over 40 years of experience and clinical investigation, I have pioneered and proven a new and completely beneficial approach to our pain that works.

I have uncovered how and why our conventional understanding of pain actually causes us to resist, suffer and deteriorate from pain. With this revolutionary and beneficial understanding of pain, we no longer suffer from pain but are relieved and developed by it whenever it is there in our lives, on any level.

In this chapter you will find your own enlightened and more complete understanding of the significance of pain and healing in your life. You are going to discover that your pain is the only thing in life you are truly scared of, for it is only when life triggers a feeling of pain or distress within you that you are then frightened of whatever triggers it. If life doesn't make you feel anything, it doesn't concern or frighten you at all. And so, what you are about to understand about pain will begin to bring that fear to an end.

Essentially, our pain and its expression is not there to hurt us but protect and heal us. It actually presents an opportunity for us to understand ourselves. All pain, physical and psychological originates as a physical bodily sensation. When felt only as that, before thought reaction occurs, the pain is usually tolerable and even a relief when experienced in its pure state.

CHECK IN WITH YOURSELF

Do you have any pain, injury or painful illness?

Do you know how to learn from and heal your pain?

Do you know what pain is really for?

Do you see pain as your enemy?

Note your answers and then put them aside whilst you complete this Chapter. At the end there will be a review of these questions to highlight your progress and help you realise the changes that have naturally happened within you in this process.

EVOLVING THROUGH PAIN

Primarily pain in the body occurs due to and accumulates from the repetition of *unnatural* attitudes and actions, beliefs and ideals that are imposed upon the human being throughout their life. All of these both cause and become harmful unnatural behaviours and actions, and accumulate massive repetitive stress in the living feeling tissue of the body. It is *this* build-up of stress that deteriorates into mental and physical pain and illness.

Wherever that stress accumulates in the body, decreased flexibility, reduced sensitivity or feeling, and the unconscious unintentional tendency to avoid or neglect that area, develops. Less vigorous use of that area results in mechanical deterioration and more susceptibility to injury during activity or from impact. This is how mental distress held in the body makes us prone to injury.

This repetition of harmful behaviours and their effects on our health is an outward expression of whatever is unclear, unknown and unresolved within us, and so actually presents an opportunity for us to understand and resolve this. Essentially, our pain and its expression is not there to hurt us more but to heal us by bringing our attention to all we have overlooked, ignored or denied about ourselves. It is from our pain that we uncover and extract the information about ourselves that is required for our full psycho-physical recovery.

RENEW YOUR RELATIONSHIP WITH PAIN

When pain, whether physical or psychological, is felt as a sensation in the body and felt only as that and as it is before thought-reaction occurs, the pain is usually tolerable and even a relief. However, our accumulated memory or experience of the pain known or unknown yet held in the body, can lead to fear or concern about a particular pain continuing. That concern of prolonged pain makes what may be tolerable right now intolerable, especially when your fear of any such prolonging is expected, anticipated or projected into a future or never-ending suffering.

To minimise your suffering to that which you—*the body*—can live with, feel and heal today, it is essential for you to stay clear on the physical facts of what is felt now and stop thinking about what was and may be again. Once you stop struggling against it and settle into accepting (not necessarily liking) the fact of your pain, your suffering decreases dramatically and often stops altogether. All that then remains is the relieving feeling of the physical sensation of the actual pain as it is, without the overwhelming misery of exaggeration caused by your thought's complaint and reaction to it. You are then ready to learn more about yourself from the true felt sense of your pain and so heal and evolve further and deeper.

Pain is there inside you due to an event that confused or hurt you, so you associate pain with being harmed. Therefore, you have an aversion to pain. Such an aversion to pain is displaced and belongs to the *time of being hurt,* not to the lingering pain itself. When your experience of being hurt is not current but is past, then the pain that *remains* is what you feel. It may be extremely distressing or frightening but it is not harming you now, it is coming out of you now, and that is healing you.

If you let that pain and any resistance to it be there, not thought about but felt, and allow whatever time it takes for it to disperse and dissolve, in its own time, it will.

We are supposed to feel pain or disturbance throughout our life and even go through minor or major healing crisis whenever they fall due and come upon us. However, our resistance to pain as part of our life has prevented our discovery of the true and benevolent nature of pain, which in turn has caused us to fear life and death and resist pain and our own complete healing now and into our future. Your renewed and enlightened relationship with pain will ultimately resolve this dilemma.

The added value of feeling and naturally healing any one aspect of your pain is that it relieves and improves your overall condition. It improves your ability and empowers your confidence to listen to your body's guidance whenever you are processing any issues or ailments in the future. And most importantly, your inevitable success from this natural approach corrects your relationship with pain or painful feelings, as you discover they are not there to hurt or harm you but to heal and guide you.

As you already know, the origin of pain is felt and known as a sensation within your body. That sensation is a disturbance or painful effect from life which you have either overlooked, denied, ignored or tried to escape or be rid of it.

Whether you have physical pain or illness or psychological pain or illness, they are actually two expressions manifesting from the same source of physical distress. When you trace either of these back to their origin, you will discover that they both originate as a physical sensation or pain felt deeper within your body. Feeling that pain at its origin in the body is how you will heal that pain or illness at its source.

ACTIVATE THE HEALING PROCESS

Pain that is felt purely as a sensation in the body is a relief to feel. But when you react mentally to it, you no longer feel it as it is. You exaggerate and intensify your overall experience of it, which overwhelms or frightens you and you then suffer the exaggeration of the pain caused by your thought-reaction to it. You don't suffer the pure and natural feeling of pain itself. When you feel that pure and natural feeling, it relieves you.

Feeling your pain purely as a sensation in your body is also what alerts and activates your body to heal itself. In fact, feeling pain is how you trigger all the natural healing processes of the body. Reacting to it, which is thinking about your pain not just feeling it, inhibits or prevents healing and even causes more harm and suffering.

When you are mentally reacting to your pain from your fears of pain or ideas or mistaken bias about pain, you also disconnect from the naturally soothing and healing feeling of it. You then begin to resist it, fight it, attack it and try to get rid of your pain or distress. All of this amounts to rejecting or attacking yourself in pain and only increases your pain or distress. So this is not the right approach to healing your pain and actually causes you to suffer a mental, emotional exaggeration of your pain.

The sensory reality of your pain, which is a relief to feel, is only felt as it truly is in and by your body, and only before you distort and exaggerate it by mentally reacting to it—by thinking about it. You will discover the reality and the original sensation of your pain beneath your suffering and conflict with it, deeper within the body.

Mixing your thinking with what you should only feel causes an exaggerated, overwhelming experience of suffering, making it difficult or even impossible to continue feeling the pain or distress as it really is. But without thought-reaction, there is no suffering, instead there is a feeling of relief and an activation of your healing.

HOW TO END MENTAL ILLNESS

Mental illness and suffering is made up of various intensities of fearing and reacting to painful and disturbing feelings or sensations, or resisting the facts of life to which you are opposed. Prolonged emotional pain is a result of that.

Once you are mentally reacting, this puts you into conflict with the physical sensations or feelings and disconnects you from the pure feeling of pain. The pure feeling of pain is actually only ever physical and never overwhelming in itself. Only our mental exaggeration of it is overwhelming.

You cannot feel with your thinking, you can only create additional distress, which is then felt in your body, additional to the actual pure sensation of pain. This addition is what you suffer as mental reaction or illness. You can only feel with and in your body, which is why only the body can heal itself. Only at that physical level can you heal pain's expression as 'mental illness' and the original pain behind the mental illness or distress.

Our additional thought-reaction to pain in life also disconnects us from the pure physicality of feeling, which deactivates our natural healing process, and then we get stuck in the suffering of our mental reaction. By contrast, feeling—physically feeling—activates our natural healing process, which purges or dissolves the feeling or the energy that drives our reactions. With no felt disturbance left to drive them, our thought-reactions then cease and so our mental suffering ends.

Then, beneath the surface of our reactionary thinking, our body's own natural healing systems are activated, and in its own time and of its own volition, we as a body can heal in every way.

HEALING OLD FEARS AND DISTURBANCES

You need to understand that the fear or even the physical pain you feel as it is purging and healing from where it has been suppressed, numbed and held in your system, is coming to life within you to heal. Unlike the pain at the time of being harmed, it is not an indication that something is wrong now. And the fear you feel is not your fear of the pain or experience you are going through to heal this, it is the old fear coming out from where it has been held or suppressed within your body. These purging sensations or unexplained feelings should not be connected to your current life circumstances or events. These feelings are what the arising pain within you is made up of and were caused by the event of the past.

Sensations that are felt during the process of healing previously suppressed pain or trauma are not indicating a problem in your life now. And it is important to not assume a connection between these feelings and anything in your life now. Also, there is no need for you to be concerned about their effect on you now. This is not pain that is harmful. This is the feeling of healing pain, which indicates a recovery, not more harm. When nothing known to you in your life now can explain why you feel the way you do, it is because these are the feelings from the past, which you are purging and healing now.

Fortunately, whether it's a mild or severe form of pain or trauma, the solution for healing it is the same. So you don't need to work out which degree of pain it is. Whichever it is, you simply need to feel it as it is to activate it, and then continue feeling it whenever it is there until it comes to its own end. Only your body knows how to fully heal itself, and it knows this in a way that is different to how we know things through thinking.

In the body, there is no reaction, no interference, only uncensored feeling all the way through the healing process to its own natural end. All you need to do is feel your pain rather than avoid or ignore or react to it by trying to get rid of it. Feel it and let your body take care of it, and it will.

HEALING EXTREME OR COMPLEX TRAUMA

The only variation on what has been explained so far is with the more extreme form of trauma or pain. Because with extreme and complex trauma there is more of it held as memory in your body, it requires more time for you to feel it to its end. And because there is more involved—more going on in the individual during more serious traumatic experiences or events—the feelings that arise during the healing of these experiences can be more confusing. It's more distressful, it's physically painful and it's more frightening, all because this is what is coming out from within you. As you feel and activate the memory held as the trauma in your body, you are now purging and healing this from where it is held in your body.

When healing past traumas, you are going through a revisiting of feelings which you have continued to suffer from or be affected by during your life. They will be either conscious, meaning known to you, or unconscious, meaning you will not know why you are that way.

Typically, when there is terror or extreme feelings reoccurring during your healing, once you begin to fully feel and purge those feelings, you can easily become confused into believing you are frightened of your pain or frightened of the process that is happening or frightened of your life now.

It is helpful to understand that you are actually feeling the extreme sensations and the fear you felt at the time of your past traumas, which is why, when you look at your life now, today, you often can't explain why you feel the way you do.

Whenever you trigger pain that has the felt memory of fear or terror within it, you will feel the activation of that fear or whatever experience the felt memory is made up of. That healing pain is made up of fear, held as tension in your body, and is now releasing. It is partially made up of the fear you were feeling during a past event, a past trauma.

If you experience this in your healing process, to enable your continued healing of such pain, it is important for you to understand that this fear is the feeling within the pain you are healing and not to get confused into thinking you are actually frightened of this healing pain, this felt memory of pain, which is the pain you are healing now. You are simply feeling the healing of fear or distress held within you as pain from a past event. This fear is not connected to your life now. When nothing known in your life now will explain why you feel the way you do, this is because it is only the memory of fear. You are not in danger now and so you only need to feel this to its end to resolve it.

Because truly feeling is deeper beneath the dramatization of thinking and emotion, you will not get caught in it. It will come to its own end by you feeling it and it will not be prolonged beyond its healthy natural duration as emotion and thinking are. You don't get caught or implode into feeling, you only get caught and lost in emotion.

You get lost in emotion because emotion is not a real response to what is real. It is a reaction to and an avoidance of what is real. It is an exaggeration of a real physical feeling. It is caused by thought's reaction to feeling or pain, or by stories about them, and so it has no end. Emotion and reactionary thinking harms you, whereas feeling the depth of physical feelings heals you.

Fortunately, thinking is only an activity of you the body that begins as a sensation in and of the body. You are the body and that is the only 'you' that can heal itself. And that happens from the inside out, originating deeper than the understanding and reach of our thought process. Healing does not happen from the outside in. Only thinking does. That is why thinking cannot heal you.

Through thinking we have created therapies which are only useful for patching us up but they don't and can't heal us. Only the body, only 'the real and living you,' actually heals anything. You are the only one who can heal you. The only one who can feel and heal your pain.

RECOVERY AS A NATURAL PROCESS

In the natural healing process, self-discovery and physical recovery are one and the same activity. They are the two parts of the natural healing process of the body. They are the body's way to both heal and enlighten itself and to return to its naturally healthy and optimal state. You feeling your pain is the alert to the body to heal itself. And as long as you feel your pain, it will. Feeling or physical sensation is the ongoing activation of any recovery, repair, or healing taking place, and is also the natural meditation of the body.

Healing yourself is not something to enforce through thought or any method or therapy invented by thought. Healing is already happening naturally of its own accord within every sensation or pain or distress felt processing within us, whenever it is necessary. It is governed by the natural intelligence of nature, of the body we are, and does not rely on other interventions other than the most mechanical and superficial, such as setting a bone or massaging a pain or tension to support or activate the healing process already ongoing within the body.

Unfortunately, the general approach of therapy or medicine is a subtle form of attack on your pain in an attempt to get rid of it rather than allow you to process and evolve through it.

In fact, it is our thought-reaction to pain or distress that has driven the invention of therapy. Therapies can be supportive during our healing and may relieve us of symptoms but the common problem is that they can more often inhibit and even prevent healing.

As our symptoms are really indications of a need for our deeper development or evolution, suppressing or soothing them with therapies disregards and interferes with the development of our physical resilience and our personal enlightenment, both of which are available to us through the processing of our pain.

The natural meditation of the body, which is to feel pain or distress and therefore heal yourself, is not enforced. It is a process that is allowed. It is allowed by our understanding that as a body, we are equipped to automatically heal from within. That us feeling our pain is the activator or trigger of that healing, and us then going through that triggered process rather than resisting it leads to our full recovery and development as an individual.

This brings an end to the chapter on pain but your opportunity to learn about pain is not yet over. Healing pain is an indicator of whatever we overlook, so to help you make the most of your learnings we will expand on all you have discovered so far by revealing the beneficial purpose of illness, and again, how to learn from it, evolve through it and subsequently heal it for yourself. It's time to move on to understanding the Significance of Illness, which is the chapter up next.

Go to the Active Meditations for this chapter in the Undo app.

PONDER YOUR PROGRESS

How would you rate your overall understanding of the significance of pain?

What did you learn to better understand the significance of pain?

Has there been any change in your attitude towards your pain?

Feel free to note any changes that you can see in yourself… subtle changes are often the deepest changes. The deepest changes are often unknown to us at the time of change and are instead only known to us as the improvements in our physical condition and the reduction of our disturbances with real life situations. So take some time out to ponder that.

NOTES:

CHAPTER ELEVEN
THE SIGNIFICANCE OF ILLNESS

NOW YOU'RE GOING TO LEARN about illness—why we have illness, and what it is really for and how you can prevent and resolve illness at its origin. This knowledge will help you to get through times of illness in your life much more easily, and to understand how to develop yourself and heal yourself through any illness. This will also negate your fear of illness and of getting sick.

To view illness as an enemy, as something to overcome, fear or avoid, or remove from our lives is a misunderstanding of the reason why we have illness and what its purpose is. Applying this misunderstanding inhibits the natural healing process and prolongs illness. And so that approach to illness can be very harmful. Illness is not a flaw to be got rid of. It is a natural and essential, inbuilt corrective crisis and a developmental process. It is a force of nature that activates from where it is deeply rooted within our own body to keep us true to ourselves. And if it is respected and followed, it prevents our decline from our original, true and natural state as an individual and a species.

CHECK IN WITH YOURSELF

Are you aware of any relationship between thinking and any sort of physical or mental illness or distress?

Note your answers and then put them aside whilst you complete this chapter. At the end there will be a review of these questions to highlight your progress and help you realise the changes that have naturally happened within you in this process.

PRESERVING OPTIMAL HEALTH

Whenever you are in psychological pain and distress, suffer physical pain or illness, or are breaking down structurally with joint or muscular problems, these are all the various indications of how the build-up of distress in your body is diminishing your health and weakening your overall system.

All signs or presence of your deteriorating health are there to bring your attention to the underlying imbalanced or inadequate manner in which you are dealing with the demands of life outside of you or the stress inside of you. These health warnings are part of your innate biological design and are essential for your wellbeing and survival. You are supposed to respond to them and be guided by them to take care of yourself. But do you know how?

To prevent prolonged illness or a permanent decline in either the physical or psychological aspects of your health, the body needs to regularly purge any build-up of stress or tension whenever these harmful effects from life form in your body. To take care of this, you need to go deeper into the source of the tensions, which are felt as the physical sensations of disturbance or anxiety or pain in the flesh of you, and recover at this point of origin of illness.

If you avoid, ignore, suppress, override or deny this early stage of developing illness, during which it is still only felt as a build-up of tensions or distress within your body, this will lead to a decline in your health and to a breakdown of the body that you are. This is how we manifest what we suffer as illnesses. But if you feel and purge the tension or distressful effects from life either as they occur or soon after, you can avoid their decline into a prolonged or more serious illness in your life. In this way you will prevent yourself suffering any significant or permanent harm by processing illness at this earlier stage.

Any imbalance in your mental or physical health clearly indicates that you are overriding or ignoring early corrective warnings, or are mentally reacting to them and so overlooking this significant guidance for maintaining your ongoing optimal health.

To correct this, consider both the mental and physical equally, originating as stress and leading to illness in your body—just as you have learnt to in the previous chapters. Without overriding or ignoring either, you will be able to detect these imbalances, which is the first step to preventing further decline. Your second step is to feel them as they are, as one sensation of distress, tension or pain within your body, to both activate their healing and be guided towards correcting any detrimental behaviour, and to evolve beyond it.

MAINTAINING A HEALTHY BALANCE

If you sacrifice your physical health to meet demands by imposing overpowering positive attitudes, eventually not only will your body break down but the accumulation of stress this causes you will lead to a gradual deterioration of your mental condition, and potentially undermine all your achievements. Or, if you sacrifice your mental health by ignoring how you feel inside, you will prolong distress in your body and that will eventually destroy your physical health, whilst also undermining your ability to sustain your achievements.

Sacrificing either aspect of your health to keep going or to continue achieving is a partial and unsustainable approach to life in general. You are missing the point. If your progress from what you do or achieve is undermined by fluctuations in your health, these are a natural warning and a self-sustaining survival instinct forcing you to find a balance between your personal wellbeing and meeting the demands of your life.

These fluctuations in your health are not your enemy. They are a warning and are ultimately essential to keep you alive and healthy now and for the long term. If you can intelligently appreciate their self-revealing significance to you and allow them to guide you into balance, you will learn all about yourself and develop into a well-balanced person in the process.

The approach of considering both your physical and mental health equally and as indicators of your entire condition is sustainable and healthy and perpetually self-illuminating. Avoiding the condition of either is no answer. To avoid them is to avoid yourself and is to override your needs and to put your health at risk.

To maintain optimal health, you need a more complete and natural bodily intelligence, which means you have to be sensitive to yourself and include and respond to your real needs. This is achieved by honest evaluation of your physical and mental wellbeing together and with equal importance. As one is also the other, to neglect either will result in the deterioration of both.

To achieve this intelligence for balance requires an ongoing sensory evaluation of yourself, through which you have a natural and automatic *feel* at all times for your condition and for your real needs. This isn't a mental state of analysis, self-obsession or self-concern. This is a natural state in which you are interconnected and sensitised throughout all of you and so have an innate and fully integrated sense of your entire condition, all the time.

WHAT IS THE PURPOSE OF MOODS?

Previously, we explored how reactionary thinking is an attempt to deny or avoid the realities of life. That emotion and emotionalising is a reaction to and an avoidance of what we truly feel but don't want to feel. These are the two ways in which we exaggerate and prolong distress and cause ourselves mental illness. We have also discussed how we can activate the primary solution to resolving both of these by acknowledging and embracing the facts of life and only feeling, not reacting to, the appropriate feelings that life stimulates automatically within us.

So you now understand how to bring an end to these unbalanced ways in which we cause and prolong our own suffering. However, to help you see the seriousness of your reactions, you also need to understand the seriousness of their effect, which is that from these psychological beginnings of prolonged reactions, your physical system is distressed and progressively damaged. This is an example of the *purely mental origin* of damage to your physical health, through causing chemical imbalance. This chemical imbalance then causes moods of *purely physical origin* that, when misunderstood, result in ongoing mental distress. With either *origin of cause*, both mental and physical illness prevails and cycles. It is important not to confuse moods with mental conditions or connect them with circumstances in your life. Moods are purely a physical imbalance and the body finding its way back to chemical balance.

From psychological origins, you suffer the *physical activation of distress* from and made up of the activity of reactionary thought. But deeper within your physical origins, you experience the quieter presence of moods. Mental illness is and originates as thought-reaction and thought-reaction's exaggeration causes its counterpart of emotion, all of which you suffer as psycho-physical distress. Although mental illness is often fuelled by suppressed trauma, trauma is not mental illness. Trauma is the physical memory of pain and harm.

The presence of trauma is evident and also known as a mood. Moods are actually a physical condition of the body—they are only felt physically. In and of itself, a mood is not actually distressful, rather it is relieving when you feel it without reacting to it, although at first this can be difficult to realise. It is your addition of thought-reaction to a mood's presence that causes any mental distress you feel and not the mood itself.

Moods emanate from the body but never exist separate to the body. They are not a mental state but a purely physical sensation, so unlike mental reactions, they do not build on themselves and cycle. Moods are a healing response of the body that resolve naturally whenever you refrain from reacting to them. Without reaction, your physical distress lessens, and your body chemistry is then able to return to its own natural balance.

The practical reason for highlighting this distinction is to help you understand that your moods are healthy healing sensations of the body and are essential to indicate and relieve the body's imbalance. So you can safely feel your moods as they are, without alarm. They are necessary for maintaining your combined and overall physical-mental health.

In contrast, the active distress of reactionary thinking indicates that you are resisting whatever you should only be feeling within yourself in order for recovery to occur. This thought-reaction is mental illness in its entirety. It is destructive to your health and prevents recovery.

Now you know more about what you're dealing with in relation to reactions and moods, you'll be more easily able to navigate through these when they occur during your healing process, making the healing journey smoother and enabling better results.

USING YOUR HEALTH AS A GUIDE IN LIFE

Both negative and positive attitudes are distorted reactions or biased opinions that we unknowingly impose on what would otherwise be normal and neutral health conditions. The apparent negative problem—in this case illness, is actually the solution yet to unfold. And so it is as much a positive as a negative.

We can only look at something as being positive because we have already viewed it as negative. But both are disconnected from the neutral reality and facts of life.

The positive is really a sneaky negative formed from the initial negative reaction. Positive thinking is both causing and sustaining the negative, and negative thinking is a result of comparing neutral reality against the unreal ideal of a positive, which then causes a third and falsified opinion towards the neutral facts of reality and makes them seem unsatisfactory or negative.

This is how the comparative, dualistic and conflicting view of opposites then blinds you to seeing the *neutral facts* of life fully and therefore discovering that everything, including your health, is actually as it should be and must be in order for it to serve as a truthful indicator and guide.

Positive and negative are both a reaction to the facts of life and both cause a distorted view of reality. They both cause a flight from reality into either optimism or pessimism and override the truthfulness of realism, which we need to reveal and guide us in the correct response to the needs of our life.

Their duality also causes a disconnection from ourselves and an emotional instability and physical distress. Whether positive or negative, both are opposing or judging otherwise neutral, harmless and essential feelings of the informative, factual and therefore neutral, conditions of life.

GUIDING YOURSELF WITH FACTS

By their very nature, facts stand alone and are non-dualistic, without a comparison or an opposite. Facts are neither negative nor positive; they are singular, neutral and real.

In reaction to the healthy presence of true feelings and stand-alone facts, our dualistic and comparative thinking combines with true and factual feelings. And as these feelings and reactions combine, this combination becomes the exaggerated distortion of emotions and of the realities of life. So as emotions are derived from reactionary thinking, they are themselves the result of our reacting to true feelings and facts. This reveals that emotions are in fact a state of reaction to the facts of life, and in a childlike fashion, we don't like them or don't want those facts to be true. And like any thought-reactions, emotions are a part of the confused states of mental illness and are harmfully prolonged by our indulgence in them.

For example, when a friend has died, rather than us accepting that unavoidable fact, we resist or deny it. We need to feel the neutral and natural feeling, and relief, of grieving to heal our pain of loss. But rather than embracing, experiencing and processing this natural feeling, we react to the loss or feeling of grief, and become emotional. And we get so caught up in our emotionalised reactions to both the fact of our loss and the appropriate feeling of grief it causes that we cause ourselves to suffer what is actually a relief to feel.

But when we accept the fact of our loss in life and the feeling of grief it causes, and feel this rather than react to it, this enables healing and resolution without prolonged pain or suffering. As reactionary thinking is itself mental illness, so too are emotions. Reactionary thinking and emotionalising have no solution or end in themselves and so if they are allowed to continue, they build up and undermine your overall health.

Whether you continue to react and resist the way you are or through positive thinking, impose force upon yourself to override this and keep going, either way you are holding the body in a prolonged state of tension. This is causing more rapid aging, decline into illness, structural problems, reduced mobility, pain and eventual misery. Then disease and death can result. Clearly neither the negative or the positive are a healthy approach, so you need to go deeper to discern and recognise the true and neutral facts of life.

Is it now clear how positives and negatives always coexist in a state of duality and conflict? Beneath their duality are your informative feelings, and beyond their conflict are undeniable facts. When you live guided by these self-evident facts of life and informed by what you truly feel, you live an awakened and simple life. This results in your ongoing self-discovery and self-understanding.

Fortunately, within all of us we have this inbuilt natural solution that reduces every single mental or physical health problem to one fundamental common source, which is felt in the body. The *physical distress you feel and sense* is the actual root of all disturbance to your health. As you know by now, if you feel the sense of that at its roots wherever it is in the body, the mental or reactionary thinking part, which is what you actively suffer, will dissipate, giving the remaining pure physical imbalance a chance to rebalance and repair itself. And with this approach it will.

RECOVERING OPTIMAL MENTAL HEALTH

Firstly, you need to understand what poor mental health or illness actually is. Poor mental health is the result of and is prolonged and continued by unresolved, underlying disturbing feelings and mental reactions either to the way you feel inside or to the facts of your life outside of you. Mental illness can also be delusional in that it is a rejection and avoidance of the real and true facts of life, simply because you don't like them or don't want them as they are or believe that you can't cope with them.

The reactionary nature of thought, combined with the rejection of real and true facts and the deeper distress of trauma from unknown causes that is suppressed and held in the body, make mental illness complex. Apart from the real feelings of underlying trauma in your body, mental illness is mostly an imaginary confusion of reality disconnected from the actual reality as it is—which is the real internal feelings and real external facts.

So, because of its complexity, its solution must be simple and must ground you in reality. It must be straight forward enough to keep you away from the complexity of the thinking you otherwise bury yourself in and suffer from. Otherwise, anything you do will only make it worse, or at least prolong it beyond its own inevitable and natural duration.

The simplicity of healing and all you need to do is own and feel your own pain. Simply through feeling is how you will heal all the complexities that come from avoiding your pain and from connecting your pain to your thoughts of not liking yourself or not liking the world around you. Grounded in these feelings from either known or unknown causes in your body, you can heal anything at all. You can trust the healing power of nature and of your body in this to resolve your mental confusion, and you will activate this power to heal simply by feeling the immediately known sensations of physical pain or illness.

Where do we go wrong?

To improve your mental health, do not apply any of traditional psychology's doctrines. Do not separate your felt sense of bodily stress, feelings or mental states into any of the labels or descriptions invented by academics or medics. Do not analyse or work out anything. Don't think up or dream up an answer to anything.

Both your analysing and the answers you invent are part of the mental trap you can get yourself in that will only confirm what you believe or think of as a problem, when it isn't. It only seems like the problem when it is actually the solution waiting to unfold the only way it can, which is through feeling and through your body's natural healing process.

Both analysing and the answers you invent are reactions to and distractions from feeling your actual pain and its resolution. Which is why the answers you invent this way can't work. As both of these are a result and symptom of your underlying distress or pain held and felt deeper in your body, no solution or end can be achieved through more of this superficial activity of thinking or analysing.

All this *thought-based* activity turns the very simple, helpful and clear into the very complex, harmful and confusing, while both causing and unnaturally prolonging your current distress. Feelings, including distress, are meant to be felt not thought about. Feeling them is the way to resolve them, and thinking prevents both feeling and resolution of that feeling.

The mechanical reason why these analytical activities intensify and sustain rather than reduce the problem, *which is really your solution*, is because they are just more *thinking*, and so are on the same shallow level—of thought—as the psychological problem being analysed. They are reactions to the problem and are therefore duplicates of the problem, duplications born of the problem. Therefore, the confused perspective they provide can only cause you to continue to perceive, confirm and treat your condition as a problem even though it isn't one.

This is why psychoanalysis is both a delusion and a trap. Also, by keeping you distracted and disconnected from the deeper *felt* distress of pain or trauma in your body, this underlying distress, which is the only real pain, and which is driving all this reactionary thinking including your need or desire to analyse, remains, and continues to drive all reaction and all mental distress and illness, without resolve.

EXITING THE TRAP OF ANALYSIS

Why is the practice of analysing a trap?

Both the *analysis* and the *believed* problem being analysed are made up of the same thoughts, which are all part of the limited thought process or concept making up the idea that you, as you are, are somehow wrong. When in fact, other than this *wrong belief* of reactionary thinking that your condition is somehow wrong, there is nothing wrong with you. The underlying and real distress felt in your body is a correct, natural and healthy response to whatever life event has caused it and wouldn't be there otherwise. Meaning, you are supposed to feel that way, at least until you heal that.

Therefore, the only solution and way out of the confusion caused by analysing or thinking about or believing your distress to be wrong lies beyond the limits of all this thought-based analysis or thinking. You have to get yourself out of this trap to realise your true wellbeing. You will achieve this by simply going deeper than all this *thinking* into the underlying felt sensations in your body.

It will also help you to realise or at least accept that, being in the state you are currently in, whenever a disturbance is triggered or ongoing within you, that disturbance is not your enemy or there to harm you but is your natural and automatic healing process actively processing, deeper within your body, right now as you are feeling it.

Then rather than reacting to however you are with analysis of it or any attempt to be different, know the solution is in realising that it is a healing or recovery already in progress and happening naturally within you. Also realise this healing activity is beyond the understanding of your thoughts about it, and so go with it by only feeling it deep within your body. And if you do react, just sink deeper, come back into the feeling of it as many times as it takes for it to eventually heal within you and in this way, it will.

HEALING THROUGH THE TRIGGERS OF LIFE

When we are in reaction, we misinterpret and so mistakenly oppose perfectly natural and appropriate responses or feelings that are stirred up from within us by life. Because we don't understand that they are determined by the intensity of a life experience, and because of our ignorance to the significance of their stimulation by life now (which is to realise their presence, feel them as they are, and proceed to heal them), we judge these felt responses as wrong, simply because we or other people don't like them. But this judgement and our struggle to be as we or others have been taught to think we should be is not realistic but idealistic. And so for real life, it is flawed. And it is this mistaken judgement that interferes with the natural healing of any internal responses or disturbances whenever they are brought to your attention by the triggers of life.

That we don't like them doesn't make them incorrect but just more difficult to face and process at first. But *feeling these* will not harm you. Only reacting to them, analysing and trying to change them will. Feeling these feelings as physical sensations or disturbances in your body is how they heal, and so this is how you will heal them for yourself. So always remember that this is just what it takes for you to heal, and most certainly, with the correct approach, you will heal.

Just by living your life day by day, unresolved states within you will always be triggered. This is how life automatically makes you aware of their presence already inside of you. Simply by feeling these, you can automatically heal and recover from the effects of your past. This is how just living your life as it is now, rather than fearing, analysing and avoiding difficulties, heals you of any harm you may have accumulated along the way.

You really don't need to think about these problems at all. Your body already has healing them covered. This is the natural and automatic response and meditation of the body. This is how you, the body, naturally heal yourself and are actually already healing yourself whenever healing is needed.

So that's quite an introduction to the significance of illness for you. When you resolve your past experiences and your current confusion about illness, this completely changes your relationship with illness. Illness for you then transforms from being an enemy or something to fear and repel to become a supportive and essential guide in your life, and an incredibly interesting exploration and personal development. Understanding illness will completely change your life experience in every way, and so now, once again this is another major turning point in your life.

In the next chapter we have the Mind Myth. This is a really interesting topic and one that will challenge one of your deepest, most destructive beliefs, but it will also greatly free you and relieve you.

Go to the Active Meditations for this chapter in the Undo app.

PONDER YOUR PROGRESS

Do you now know that the reason you cannot change yourself is because you are not supposed to?

Do you now understand that only your learned bias about yourself can and should change for you to know and appreciate yourself as you are?

Do you know that without that learned bias there is no way for you to dislike yourself and that without it, you will be perfectly fine with yourself however you are?

Feel free to note any changes that you can see in yourself… subtle changes are often the deepest changes. The deepest changes are often unknown to us at the time of change and are instead only known to us as the improvements in our physical condition and the reduction of our disturbances with real life situations. So take some time out to ponder that.

NOTES:

_____

_____

_____

_____

_____

_____

_____

_____

_____

_____

_____

CHAPTER TWELVE
THE MIND MYTH

THE NEXT, EVEN DEEPER STEP in the journey of reconnecting your whole self, centres on the understanding of the 'mind myth' which is revealed in this chapter. The topic is quite challenging to a very confusing and harmful belief that most of us have. But once you begin to understand what I'm talking about, you will start to see yourself and life more clearly and simply. You will be more able to naturally experience how every part of you is connected and functioning as one whole organism. As this new understanding begins to penetrate any deeply ingrained beliefs in a mind, it will uproot them, leaving you free of the many problems they cause.

All activity we accredit to a mind or spirit is purely the live physical mechanics of your body. You only think there is a mind because you don't fully understand these live mechanical functions that are going on throughout the body of you. This chapter challenges a belief-based indoctrination that for generations has slipped through the guard of intelligent enquiry. I will endeavour to demonstrate why and how this one belief is the most inhibiting of all intangible beliefs, as well as how it overpowers rationality and contradicts otherwise obvious and tangible facts.

CHECK IN WITH YOURSELF

What do you think the mind is?

Where do you think it exists?

Have you ever found it within yourself?

What do you think its function is?

Note your answers and then put them aside whilst you complete this chapter. At the end there will be a review of these questions to highlight your progress and help you realise the changes that have naturally happened within you in this process.

UNCOVERING GENERATIONAL INFLUENCE

When an unproven idea is both repeatedly heard and casually spoken of throughout the course of your life, it becomes so familiar to you that you accept it as true without realising, and without really knowing for yourself whether it is true. When your family, surrounding culture or society have accepted and repeated an idea, the combined atmosphere of generational acceptance and the repeated reference to that idea is heard, absorbed and unquestionably accepted by you over your lifetime. Even if—as it is with the mind—the idea has no tangible merit in reality, without any serious consideration of your own, you accept it without thinking about it further or feeling a need to question it.

Consequently, growing up surrounded by these influences, even intelligent people tend to form beliefs in all sorts of nonsense without even realising it, and truly believe these beliefs to be their own understanding when they are not.

You have built your identity of yourself and determined your personal values out of these influences. Because of this, some personally challenging realisations and the recognition of your own confusions, where these have occurred, are going to be required for you to exit from these lifelong influences. Then and only then, without these influences, can your own enquiry begin.

As you begin to challenge and break free of these deeply engrained influences, you will naturally begin to think for yourself on all matters. You will discover that virtually everything you have taken for granted and thought to be factual, everything you have learnt from society and believed to be your own thoughts, is in fact mostly the imaginings and biases you have learned from other people.

Cultures and the blinding disinformation of repeated beliefs are passed along, and continue to stifle individuality, through repetition and influences imposed upon your innocence in childhood and until now. This is how the originality of your natural genius and its inbuilt solutions for life, and your capacity to simply think for yourself, are systemically drowned out by nonsense. Long term, your ability to think freely for yourself, to solve your own problems and to know and think your own thoughts, is lost.

KNOWING WHEN YOU'RE UNDER INFLUENCE

When you can no longer discern your own thoughts from what others have influenced you to think, you have lost the essential ability to think for yourself and to know yourself and life afresh, untainted by how you have been influenced to see them. When what you think is no longer derived from your own personal discoveries, your thoughts are no longer your own.

These casually ingrained second-hand beliefs and ideas form as our unknown or unconsciously accepted beliefs. They form our bias and defensive opinions. They then become what we think we actually know without us even realising that they are only *our beliefs*. These beliefs and ideas elude us, because they exist under the surface of our conscious thinking as the reactionary patterns and disturbances held within our bodies. It is from there that they influence what we feel and what we think we know, when in truth we don't know at all.

The indication that we are under the influence of this type of ingrained bias or belief is that we feel defensive against any challenge to them. It is often only when these hidden beliefs are challenged, and the underlying feeling of defence and strong opinion then flares up within us, that we can know we are indoctrinated and limited by them.

So notice whenever you feel defensive. This will likely be an indication or warning of an idea you are stuck in, and from which you need to free yourself in order to break free of learnt and biased influences. To give yourself the greatest chance to discover this freedom, make sure you really consider the validity and value of whatever challenges you before you decide for or against it.

UNDO THE BELIEF IN A MIND

Whenever you notice a warning sign that you are under influence, this is a tremendous opportunity for insight into yourself. At these moments, you can both realise and purge the influence to recover your own inquisitive intelligence, and your capacity for discovery and for thinking thoughts of your own.

The indoctrination into the myth of a mind has slipped through intelligent enquiry for generations and is one of the most inhibiting and destructive of beliefs. It is the foundational reason why you fall prey to the influence of many other debilitating beliefs. This is because your belief in a mind disconnects you from the sensory life and intelligence of the body. This desensitising effect then makes you vulnerable to other untrue and unnatural influences.

The negation of the belief in a mind will likely be the most challenging aspect of Undo that you have progressed through so far. But it will also have the most liberating and far-reaching effect of any that you have been exposed to here so far. Breaking free of this belief, you will integrate within your live physical self, which in turn awakens the sensitivity of your natural bodily intelligence. And it is this sensed intelligence that will keep you immune to other false and harmful influences.

At this point, I encourage you to beware of any hasty rejections of this information that may be flaring up from within you, and to thoroughly consider the value of this very challenging topic. Just keep going, staying open to the possibility of discovering something vastly new. Stay open to whatever you can't fully understand yet. Make use of all the meditations in the app and the many ways we have shown you to test and explore whatever you find challenging, if and as you need to. I am not interested in replacing your old ideas with new ones but only in you thinking for yourself. And you being free of old ideas is a part of what it takes for you to be able to do this. So stay open to the challenges and let yourself be free to experiment and discover for yourself, and ultimately, to be solely and uniquely you.

MY NATURAL RESET

My initial discovery of the mind being a myth came upon me naturally during prolonged periods of simply sitting still. It occurred as a series of eruptions from within my body that continued over a few years. That process eventually released all the deeper tensions of memory that held any ideas I had formed of myself and the world, from whatever had been imposed on me by others throughout my life.

This was a massive natural reset, a process that left me highly sensitised to myself and the world as it really is. Meaning, the world as it is known sensorily and in the body, before adding any of thought's interpretations or preferences to it.

Another very significant and beneficial change that occurred from this reset was that my system developed an accelerated response of recovery from any and all harmful life effects. This has kept me unusually resilient and healthy ever since. The overall physiological change put me on the cutting edge of discovery in the areas of life I have been sharing with you, and I have lived there ever since. From that point on, I have been helping others to regain their own natural robustness and health. Through this work, I have proven that it is not only possible for others to do this, but that this natural resilience and healthiness is in fact natural to all of us.

It was very clear to me that my newly developed accelerated and natural ability to recover was directly linked to the ending of my own imagined division within myself between a mind and a body. This helped reveal to me that the primary reason for poor health in all of us is in fact rooted in the unfeeling disconnection this imagined division causes within us. It also revealed that by bringing an end to the unfeeling disconnection the belief in this myth causes, anyone is able to live as a whole and singular, extraordinarily healthy, self-repairing being.

The simple reason for this is of course that the primary activator of the healing force of nature, and therefore recovery from any ailment, is us purely physically feeling the felt sensations within us.

Further evidence of this revelation on health has occurred during the few times in my life that I have become injured or ill or distressed. At these times, I was always able to trace the illness, injury or distress back to a disconnection, to where something within me was unfelt. And resolving that disconnection always resulted in my rapid, often instant, recovery. Whether it was recovery from structural ailments, internal illness or mental distress, my reconnection with the underlying feelings behind these always resulted in complete recoveries.

Ironically, and more directly related to mental health or sanity, my discoveries of what isn't truly there to be truly known have been the most freeing and enlightening, and yet the most challenging to communicate.

IDENTIFYING AND INTEGRATING THE BODYMIND

When the body expresses itself in feelings, thoughts and words, through imagination or from memories, we call that activity 'the mind'. However, the object of the idea we call the mind is actually the body. And all the activity we accredit to the mind is purely and simply physical mechanics.

Confusion has arisen from us overlooking these functions of the body, and that their expression is actually our flow of natural bodily intelligence originating purely as sensations. This oversight has only arisen because of our desensitisation to these underlying sensations of the body as they form their expression into more complex feelings, thoughts and words. Due to our disconnection from these ongoing origins of thought, and its development from sensations into thoughts and words, we mostly only notice the final part of this process, as ourselves thinking.

In our disconnected numbness to our physical origins and self, it seems to us as though thinking miraculously appears out of nowhere, and so we find ourselves unnecessarily confused about where thinking comes from, and what *does* the thinking.

Because we are disconnected from our own whole function of the way we come into the expression of ourselves—from sensations through to our expressions of those sensations in our life—we live in confusion about this. And out of that confusion, we have invented a *mysterious mind entity* that, in our ignorance of ourselves, we think the body needs to do its thinking for it.

Overlooking the obvious within ourselves, we have missed the only knowable physical functions that develop into thinking, and therefore explain away the need for an additional imagined thinker of our thoughts, which we call our mind.

We live oblivious to the knowable and discernible fact that thought and thinking is itself a function of the body. This is because we do not know that the origin of thought is physical sensations. Or that these originally felt sensations both precede and also become our thoughts, which then become our expression as words or information.

Overlooking the knowable, we invent the unknowable. Then looking outside and beyond the knowable for the answers that are already within our own body, we distract ourselves with myths and religions, spiritualities and psychologies in search of answers we already know and only have within us. Then, in endless searching for these creations of our own imagining, we lose our sanity and the simple truths of ourselves, of what we are and how we function, and also of how to take care of ourselves.

WHEN IS BELIEF APPROPRIATE?

An example of when belief is appropriate is our reliance on physicians who have dissected the body to inform us of the various organs that are inside our bodies. We are happy to believe there is a heart, lungs and so on inside our bodies because our belief is based on the physicians' repeated physical discoveries. We don't know for ourselves, and we cannot without dissecting a corpse ourselves, but because we have the physicians' factual and physical evidence, it is rational to accept their claims to be a true understanding of some of what exists within our own body.

But passed down and learned from the spiritualists, the majority today claim the existence of a mind. But this is no more than a modified belief in a spirit or soul, and even after centuries of dissections, it has never been found. From the perspective of any genuine scientific method and the evidence of reality itself, we have actually discovered and proven the mind's absence.

Yet both our students and experts of the science of mental health claim to have studied and understood the workings of this intangible mind. But how can they sincerely claim to have studied it if they can't even find it?

Consequently, the services we have developed in our attempts to cure and alleviate health problems of this elusive part of us have failed. For how do you study, treat or cure a condition of something that can't even be found or confirmed to exist?

Is this good enough?

Is this really any different to religions, mysticisms or superstitions?

Is it scrupulous to base a culture and health industry on a make believed body part?

If our students of mental health were to realise that the object of their study and the behaviours they observe are not of this fabricated mind but are entirely of the body itself, then the possibility for the much-needed advancement in their understanding would begin. They could emerge from the dark ages of the confusion and ineffectiveness caused by belief in disembodied spirits and minds. They could then drop the impossible task of trying to study the non-existent and focus on something real—the embodied mind—the feeling thinking body.

Then they could begin to discover the origins of and solutions to our mental health problems within the real and existing body. And with something tangible to study and understand, they might even begin to solve real and existing problems and be fulfilled by that achievement. Frustrations and vagueness would be replaced with certainty, as their task would become clear through them truly knowing what they are studying and treating. This would open up a genuine and unique science grounded in tangible and applicable understanding, and would provide them with a real object of focus—the body.

UNDERSTANDING HOW WE FUNCTION

It is important to understand that the study of ourselves is unique to all other studies and all other sciences. It requires us or its students to go beyond the current scientific method of external observation and evaluation based in thinking, which is only useful for everything outside of ourselves. When it comes to ourselves, there is a totally different need and fortunately, there is the unique capacity to fulfil that need.

The need is to penetrate the direct experience within ourselves and for ourselves. For this is in fact the only way to understand what we are and how we work. And so, we can only do this for ourselves. No one else can do it for us. Nor can we do it for anyone else if it is to mean anything to them or have any self-illuminating impact on them.

We are the only thing in existence with which we can take this direct and unique approach, and consequently, the only thing we can understand to this depth.

Only within ourselves can we directly feel and experience our own existence as it is, and therefore know ourselves exactly and purely as we are. And until we understand ourselves to this depth, we do not truly know or understand ourselves with certainty, nor in a way that makes any significant difference.

We do not need and cannot use thought for this and in fact, only without thinking about it can what we feel and therefore know remain untainted and known as it is.

There is actually nothing else in existence which we can directly know in this absolute and truly confirmable way.

We ourselves are the only thing in existence which we can and do feel and know from the inside out.

And we are the only thing we can know without the guess work of observation or the potential bias and misinterpretations of our thinking.

And we can do this by simply being ourselves.

This is why it is only with ourselves that we have this ability to confirm and truly know what we discover.

We cannot be this certain with anything else but ourselves.

CLARIFYING THE ORIGIN OF BEHAVIOURS

Unable to find a mind, in order to study it or even validate its existence, the experts have resorted to studying and analysing what they have assumed and believed to be expressions of a mind—human behaviours and its various expressions. But they have deceived themselves and the world at large by pretending to *know* this as fact when actually they can only be *believing* that a mind is both responsible for, and the origin, of those behavioural activities.

They have no factual evidence of a mind and therefore can't know or confirm that human behaviours are linked to a mind, produced by a mind or have anything to do with a mind. All of that which they have assumed and claimed to be the activity of the mind, they have then used to provide false evidence of its apparent existence.

Even when we study human behaviour, we don't have any way to know or confirm that these behavioural expressions indicate the existence of a mind, or that a mind has anything to do with them, or that behaviours are driven by or have anything to do with a mind. Because we have lacked a deeper exploration and any proper intelligent consideration, we have only *assumed this connection,* and then have proceeded without realizing or admitting to our assumption.

This oversight can easily happen with unchallenged ideas that we naïvely accept and then repeat over time. We explored earlier in this chapter how ideas become so familiar to us that their assimilation into our daily lives go unnoticed. And how we forget that we never really got around to confirming them, or questioning their validity, and ended up just accepting them without proof. Their familiar presence throughout our lives in both written and spoken words escapes our discernment between reality and idea. This is one way that belief systems penetrate societies. The mind myth is but one of them. But a very serious one, as you are progressively discovering.

TRACING BEHAVIOUR BACK TO PHYSICAL SENSATION

As there is no mind to be found and only a body is present, then human behaviours can only be to do with the body. When our behaviours are clearly recognisable as bodily functions, these bodily activities can no longer be used as grounds to support the existence of a mind. This leaves no remaining false or confusing evidence of a mind at all.

On this solid, physically tangible and knowable premise—that the mind is in fact the body—we are only dealing with the body, with one singular entity. And so we not only have something that exists and so is tangible to study, but we also have much more to work with towards understanding human behaviours, mental illness and its treatment and cure. If its treatment and cure is even required at all. For the idea of an illness and a separate cure actually changes as we understand what we are truly dealing with, and as the beneficial reasons for these so-called ailments are revealed.

Our relationship with and view of sickness is completely changed by our discovery of the significance of mental and physical illness, and of how we can evolve through these. What is also revealed includes the true significance of all human behaviours and expressions. They are all equally important and informative expressions of the body. They are never defective, only our misunderstanding of their significance and of what they are telling us has been. They reveal our deepest needs and guide our various recoveries and self-corrections from the inevitable effects of life as we live it.

Our common failure to cure mental illness clearly indicates that at this point in time, we don't yet understand it. That which we understand, we develop through and so cure. So the fact that we cannot yet cure an ailment just shows that we don't understand it, not that it can't be cured, healed or resolved. During my discoveries of this natural approach and while helping tens of thousands of people to actually recover from whatever ailed them, I have always found this to be so, without exception.

How can we, and more importantly, why do we claim to understand the mind when it eludes our discovery of its very existence.

Why do we pretend to know?

Why do we, as both ordinary and extraordinary people, believe that *the experts* know?

This is how people, regardless of their intelligence, give their power away and suffer misguidance in their lives. But now it's time you found out for yourself. That's how you will enhance your intelligence, break free of others' influence and take back your power. Power to plumb the depths of your own sensations of knowing for and from yourself, and from this, regain the power to think for yourself, to discover and know for yourself. This is our responsibility to ourselves and to one another. This is your absolute responsibility to yourself.

UNLEASH YOUR CAPACITY FOR GENIUS

Sensing, feeling, thinking, knowing, memory, imagination and communication are all functions of the body, but because we don't realise this or how these functions work, and because we haven't recognised the tangible physical processes that are responsible for these functions, what we have, put simply, is a poor understanding of our own body's functions and capabilities. So our need is to discover more, not just imagine more.

Is it acceptable to deny our poor understanding and just imagine and pretend the answer is an *elusive thing*—an unknowable and non-existent mythical mind?

Of course it isn't acceptable. In fact, it is very harmful and stupefying to do so. Only if we admit our ignorance, admit to not knowing, can we unleash our capacity to discover something new to us, and real. Otherwise, we can't, and we won't.

As this particular ignorance of an imaginary mind has such detrimental effects, discovering and understanding the truth of the matter is hugely significant for everyone. The suffering and misery of millions can be resolved once we understand the problem, and therefore the solution, of where and what it is.

You will always find the solution within your pain and distress—felt within your body. And you will activate its healing by feeling your pain and not from any approach to avoid it or be rid of it. Disconnecting from the pain you feel in your body into the many mental reactions you have to it, into what momentarily exists as what we call *mind*, is the behaviour that causes the addition of mental illness or distress. This avoidance of making contact with and knowing your actual condition prevents the activation of healing and of any related personal development that is required for you to evolve beyond your current condition.

The degree of ongoing harm that this massive oversight and cultural indoctrination is responsible for will only really be known to you once you make this discovery for yourself and reap the resulting benefits, which I can assure you are massive, and so far for me, are endless.

But before pointing the finger at the experts or the medical or religious professions, take back the responsibility for your own part in this, in letting yourself down by believing others. First ask yourself one thing.

Do *you know* whether there is a mind?

Or have you just gone along with this idea without truly considering it?

Have you ever *asked yourself, "Is there a mind?"*.

Probably not. If you have not, why not?

For the same reason no one else has, *including* the experts—generational indoctrination.

TRUSTING IN YOUR SENSE OF KNOWING

Academics and others who are unable to discern between believing something and knowing something have claimed to know, and possibly sincerely believe they do know, what can only be believed. This confusion between believing and actually knowing for yourself, and the broad acceptance of believing over truly knowing is the flaw within academic and religious thinking. This confusion between knowing and believing has the effect of causing false generational beliefs and social conditioning.

But it is important to understand that it is the imaginings of ideologies themselves that harm us. The academics, experts on the mind and preachers of beliefs systems are also victims of the beliefs they deliver.

To be open to realising that you only believe something but don't really know it for yourself is a big step, and a blow to your ego. But it is essential if you are to break free of what you have studied and believed—of what you have believed from what others have told you. It is important not to feel criticised or to criticise ourselves or others over whatever we have believed.

For they are long term generational indoctrinations which no one has asked for, but having these imposed on us since childhood is sociably acceptable. This itself is an indication of the unenlightened and dark age we have all been living through and have a need to break out of.

Ideas have been very overpowering for our species. In avoidance of the raw realities of our natural world and the difficulties of life itself, we have become addicted to the denials and escapes of overthinking and the soothing numbness of fantasy. Our avoidances and these blinding and numbing beliefs destroy our individual intelligence and our ability to heal ourselves. They inhibit anything new and original.

Whatever beliefs or ideas you are enslaved to, these also enable others to exert the power of their influence over you. This is the result of repeating your ideas without truly finding out for and from yourself. And the idea of a spirit or mind is one of the most significant and most harmful escapes from reality out of all of them.

And it happens as simply as this. Because we have heard about a mind and have then spoken of it as though it exists, like any idea repeated over time, it becomes commonly accepted as true. Such common knowledge is also common ignorance, and once *commonly accepted*, it then becomes unacceptable for anyone to critique it or question it. Entire institutions, including our societies and cultures, are built on it, *so how could it be untrue?* But it is. This type of influence is the cause and meaning of any dark age of ignorance and human decline, like the times we now find ourselves in, but which you may now find yourself exiting, right now.

And now that you know this, is it acceptable for you to continue to live this way? Well now you have the choice. Fortunately, now you don't have to.

REMOVING DEPENDENCY ON OTHERS

We should apply a broad and empathetic understanding of our gullibility in believing in a mind. The precedence for this belief has been indoctrinated into our species for thousands of years by religion and spiritualism. Mind, psyche, soul or spirit… it's all the same theme, simply modified to continue in the same vein for yet another era of humankind.

The witch doctor became the priest, the monk, the healer, the shaman, and again the doctor, and eventually the modern-day healers are now the ones who imagine they are treating a mind. They have overlooked that it is only a function and not something that exists that can be treated. And we all go along with it and become dependent on them for guiding and healing us. But they can't heal us. Like the rest of us, they too have been indoctrinated over time and have forgotten how to heal themselves.

As a consequence of this age of ignorance to our own natural abilities, where even the healers are sick and have forgotten how to heal themselves, the accepted decline of our species' sanity and health has accelerated. Now the many unhealed healers are leading others into further dependency and decline.

We are the only ones who can heal ourselves but by relinquishing our sole responsibility to ourselves in this, over time, we have forgotten how to. And so, with no one left to heal us, it is now time to turn back to ourselves and rediscover how to.

How?

By dropping these failed belief systems, these beliefs in things that don't exist or work, and learning from the facts of life, from what is self-evident and equally knowable to us all.

By finding the answers for yourself within the live and intelligent organism you are.

By discovering how every expression of your body is a guidance for your wellbeing and optimal survival, uniquely tailored for you, from you, as part of the ongoing expressions of the body of you.

By realising that any separation and desensitisation from yourself as a body is the primary cause of all weakness, confusion, decline and disease and susceptibility to harmful influence.

These are your first steps in reclaiming your independence and power to heal yourself.

To recover from this division and dissociation from yourself, don't ignore the evidence that this belief in a mind has been accepted by you or any one of us. This evidence is that, even though neither you nor anyone else can locate it, it had never occurred to you to ask for yourself, *"Is there such a thing?"*. Or why you have never thought to sense inside, to ask and discover within yourself, *"Where within me does thinking truly come from?"*.

That these questions had never occurred to you only reveals that you have been under the influence of a powerful and harmful belief.

This passive acceptance of any delusion is not okay. It indicates that a repetitive, hypnotic and generational programming has been taken on within you. Its debilitating, dulling effects on your natural intelligence are evident in that you have not been deeply concerned to find your way out of this confusion, or thought to question this before.

But it's not too late to begin. And it's not your fault. It happened historically to us all. It's the underestimated power and devastating effects of the ignorance that is caused when generational conditionings are passed along through family, culture, education and belief systems.

By forgetting that we are simply another creature who shares this planet with many other creatures, creatures that are more like us than in our ignorance we have imagined, and then believing ourselves to be superior, we have divided ourselves from our natural world.

Consider the harm, the massive limitations that have been caused, and the false authority that has been given due to our historic belief in a mind. Our current day psychological belief system is a mere 100 years old. It is infantile in its development yet follows in the footsteps of centuries of religions that promote and thrive on this very same crippling theme of a belief in another you, additional to the natural person you are.

Most important to you in all of this though, is the effect you have on yourself as a result of no longer thinking for yourself and finding out from yourself. What is important is ending your crippling dependency on others who themselves are also unknowingly crippled by the same beliefs.

To go deeper on this topic, open yourself to this question of the existence of a mind and to your unrealised beliefs in it by digging into the many ways this belief has affected you.

Begin to notice and pay attention to whenever you casually and regularly refer to this non-existent mind, as though it exists. And seriously consider how by doing so, you continue to embed it within you and remain under its harmful influence.

As you can see, this topic is no small matter. The mind, soul, spirit or consciousness theme is the absolute foundation on which all delusions, belief systems or disconnections from your reality rest, it can be fundamentally challenging to any underlying or known belief. The Mind Myth is possibly the most challenging of all the chapters so far. Without this one belief in a second self, all the soothing escapes from the raw facts of life, all imagined alternatives to our known and knowable reality, simply fall apart.

Next is the chapter on Stop Harming Yourself. It's a logical, straightforward one to comprehend, but it can be quite tricky in that it requires a genuine and keen interest to master. But the benefits are massive if you implement it into your life, and once again it has life changing consequences.

Go to the Active Meditations for this chapter in the Undo app.

PONDER YOUR PROGRESS

Describe what you now understand to be the purpose of thought in your life?

Describe what you understand as the purpose of sensations and then feeling in knowing yourself and understanding all life.

Did you set out to change these things or did they just happen on their own, simply by you hearing this information and doing this chapter?

Feel free to note any changes that you can see in yourself… subtle changes are often the deepest changes. The deepest changes are often unknown to us at the time of change and are instead only known to us as the improvements in our physical condition and the reduction of our disturbances with real life situations. So take some time out to ponder that.

NOTES:

_____

_____

_____

_____

_____

_____

_____

_____

_____

_____

CHAPTER THIRTEEN
STOP HARMING YOURSELF

W E'RE NOW GOING TO COMBINE all that you've learned so far into one simple solution that will help you immensely, and for your entire life. You already understand that accumulated tensions or feelings in the body determine how it feels to be you. And you understand that those distressful sensations or feelings drive harmful behaviours or actions that can rule or sabotage you in life.

In this chapter we'll be showing you how to reclaim and integrate those parts of yourself. This will enable you to end what drives you from within to harm yourself or others. To be more whole, and to then live more fully, optimally and successfully in every way, more than you ever could before.

If *you* can't stop harming yourself, you have no chance of stopping others from harming you or you from harming them. This chapter offers an approach to recognising, understanding and ending self-harm. This approach will empower you towards self-reliance, sustainable health and the maturity that is required to address and end harm for all of us. Understanding the origin of what makes you harm yourself or others and resolving that at its source within you, is what will end the harm.

CHECK IN WITH YOURSELF

It is valuable to be open to questioning whatever you do that may be harmful to yourself or others. Not to use this to judge yourself, but so that you can begin to connect with the pain that is driving the harm from within you, and to heal this.

Do you know the things you are currently doing to harm yourself?

Ask yourself, "What are the ways I harm myself, internally or externally each day in life?"

Note your answers and then put them aside whilst you complete this chapter. At the end there will be a review of these questions to highlight your progress and help you realise the changes that have naturally happened within you in this process.

LEARN HOW THE HARM CAN STOP WITH YOU

In the old days, people in the west went to church one day a week to repent their sins for the other six days of the week and then repeated this process the next week. Why didn't they just stop doing harm? Because, just like people today, they didn't know why they did what they did, what drove them from within or how to stop it. And blaming the devil didn't help them or prevent the inherited generational pain that followed. And here we are today!

Sometimes the pain or feelings that drive you from within do feel as though you are possessed and overpowered, and the actions from these are devastating. Right there is our only demon, and it isn't fictional or evil, but real. It is not separate to us and beyond our power, but something we can deal with and resolve. However, inventing a fictional devil separate to ourselves to blame is just denial and giving our power away to fear. This stupid and stupefying answer prevented millions of people, for thousands of years, from looking any deeper than these ideas. It also prevented them from discovering the answer and solution to this—of healing their own pain, rather than blaming others or acting it out and doing more harm—and so the misery has continued.

Isn't it about time we found the way to stop the excuses and the harm? Well, now you have. And now that you know how to, an unprecedented and massive change in direction can begin with you and can begin with all of us. Then generations to come can inherit the benefits of our own healing, rather than reap the pain of our continuing cycle of harm.

Now that you know how to resolve this within yourself, not resolving this, and therefore continuing the harm, is not an option you will be able to comfortably live with. Only you can make a difference. This is not a dreamy ideal but the only realistic response to the immediate needs of our species and our world. Right now, any one of us can make a significant difference for ourselves, and in the world we live in, for the people we interact with and the generations we precede.

Understand that any discomfort you feel as a result of you not embracing this, and therefore continuing the harm, is not caused by your judgement of yourself but is indicating the return of your natural intelligence. Any discomfort you feel with continuing to be harmful—from its origin in you and outward towards others and the world—is essential. That discomfort is what will guide, protect and prevent you from continuing in this way.

RESOLVING HARMFUL CONTRADICTIONS

Today, people exercise to manage their stress or because they want to be slimmer or healthier, but then they continue to think harmful thought patterns, overeat or consume toxic junk in contradiction.

Do they want to be fat or slim, healthy or sick?

So many people spend so much money going to a multitude of therapists to relieve their illness, pain or distress, and when the band-aid falls off, they continue with the behaviours that caused their suffering of poor health and the need for relief in the first place.

Do they want to heal or harm themselves? It makes no sense at all.

That is, until you realise that most of us are confused divided contradictions of ourselves. We have both the urge to harm ourselves and care for ourselves at once. Because we want two opposing things at once, life is a virtual stalemate and therefore exhausting for us.

On the surface, we don't want to be fat, unhealthy, distressed, poor or mean to ourselves or others. So why don't we stop all the things that we do to cause all this trouble in our lives? On the surface, we care and it matters to us but underneath the surface, we sabotage ourselves, tell ourselves we don't care or that it doesn't really matter, or trick ourselves with the short-sighted excuse that 'we've got to have a bit of fun'. But how can it be fun if it's also harmful, unless you are demented. Or is there something more in this?

If you are sensitive to and therefore sufficiently intelligent to understand the harm your actions are causing you or others, then you can't continue with such actions. But when you are desensitised to these effects, you won't have or *feel* any natural concern or remorse, and without that, you won't always succeed in stopping self-harm or the harm you do to others, even if you really want to.

Due to us disassociating from ourselves in so many ways, we have lost our natural governing aversion to harm, which we require to prevent us harming ourselves and others.

Lacking both sensitivity and an intelligence that is natural in a whole and healthy person, we find ourselves split in two, living as a divided contradiction of a person.

In this state we want more than one thing at a time. When two or more opposing desires operate within you at once, you will find life very hard. Your *whole* thinking is confused, conflicted and contradicts with what you say and know you want to do. You put energy into one direction in your life only to sabotage that through opposing and contradictory attitudes, beliefs, words or actions. You breathe fresh air because naturally, you want to feel alive, but then smoke cigarettes which suppress how you feel, because perhaps at some hidden level, you want the part of you in pain to die. You nurture your health then you abuse it. You care for and support your children, partner, friends or colleagues, and then you unload your pain on them and destroy any benefit from your support. You advance in one area and undermine yourself in another. You live as two people, a contradiction, a self-saboteur.

GAINING A UNIFIED SENSE OF YOURSELF

Truly considering and then remaining aware of two basic facts will help you to both feel more responsible and care more when these harmful tendencies come over you.

Fact 1: Did you know or realise that whatever you feel, think, say or do has an immediate effect on both yourself and on others, and on your whole environment?

Fact 2: Did you know that you cannot remain unaffected by others or your environment? Whether you notice this effect or not depends on how numb or switched off you are—or aren't.

The relevance or lesson in this is: If I harm me, I harm you. If I harm you, I harm me. If I refuse to harm me, I won't so easily let you harm me, and I won't be so comfortable harming you.

The healthier and more grounded in my body I become, eventually my discomfort with harming you in any way will feel worse than my urge to harm you. And my newly revived humane sensitivity, which shows itself in this discomfort, will prevent me from harming you or me.

So how do you exit the contradiction and stop all this exhausting harm to yourself and to others?

By integrating both sides of yourself and recovering your whole sense of self in and as the body. This includes two simultaneous processes. In the first, you drop or negate the influences that you have taken on from others throughout your life. Influences that have formed into your idea of yourself, which has then dominated and disconnected you from your own true sense of yourself, in the body. This we have covered thoroughly in previous chapters.

The second process is you going deeper into the physical feeling of yourself, deep beneath any influences or ideas about yourself, into the body of you. This is where you will regain and build on your true sense of yourself, already existing within the body.

Once you are back in contact with yourself, this overarching process of integration must happen of its own volition, without criticism of either side or of any part of you. Intelligent, sensitive consideration of both sides equally results in your integration into a singular and united whole self. This approach alone will end the contradiction. Consequently, you will be able to purge and so stop the harm at its origin, where it begins as a disturbing sensation within you. Then healthy actions will resume, naturally, without the need for force.

WHERE TO BEGIN TO HEAL THE HARM

So that you are more able to refrain from feeling bad about yourself, and from harming yourself through self-judgement or criticism, it is important that you understand the following. There is a significant reason why you are mean or harmful to yourself or others, and that is because there is pain within you that is beyond your control, and even beyond your conscious awareness. Therefore, your choice of whether to act on your pain or not is usually beyond you until you understand and heal your condition further.

This is especially for those of you who have suppressed trauma inside of you. If you are harmful, this is an indication that you are harbouring suppressed harm within you. So remember this as you learn more from the following information, and as you study the other parts of this chapter. And be patient with yourself. Don't be harsh on yourself. This information is not to be used against yourself but to help you find your way free of harm.

Trauma will be the reason why you are unable to connect, feel empathy or stop the harm at first. You will not be able to stop yourself from expressing harmful words or actions when harm is still suppressed or held within you. So don't be too hard on yourself. You are not bad or evil even though sometimes your actions may be or at least seem so, and you may think poorly of yourself at times. If you do dislike the way you are sometimes, this actually means that you are less disconnected than you could be. At least you feel something. But either way, whether you dislike the way you are or not, remember that you are this way because you are hurt and damaged from life.

If you cause harm, just feel the distress when you realise what you have done, or after you do it, or just feel how numb you are if that is how you feel. Punishing yourself or feeling guilty won't help. Feeling cold, numb or upset from the outcome of your pain may be all you can do for now. If so, that's fine. That's where you begin.

You know you are numb because you feel numb. That may be all feeling is for you for now when you are feeling these hurt and potentially harmful parts of you. That's enough to progress from. In time, the numbness will resolve, and you will begin to feel the pain and distress you were previously numb to. Then, over time, the more you feel the pain or distress, just as you have been learning to, the easier it will become for you to contain those feelings within you, rather than react outwardly and harm yourself or others.

At first, you will not realise the harm you cause around you from the harm within you, because you have learnt to ignore or justify it. Even if you are numb or unaware of harm or pain within you, by noticing your effect on others, you can begin to realise when something is wrong.

But you still won't know how to change or prevent these ingrained behaviours. And you can't always be sure it's you, even when it is, because you aren't yet connected enough with what's inside you to know for sure and know for yourself.

Also, a side effect of the harm you have suffered is that you can't really trust anyone, or you find it very hard to. And so even when others complain about your behaviours, often you just can't see the problem they claim to see. There are many blind spots and confusions that come with being traumatised. And a great deal of confusion comes from how disconnected we then become to our own condition, as we try to survive through our lives. Only as we begin to recover from the harm do we then begin to recover the full picture or memory of what our life has really been like.

HOW DISTRESS STOPS HARM

You will generally feel confused or bad when you act out your pain, or you may feel unfairly judged by others when you do so if you don't or can't yet realise that you have been doing this. It is important to not think badly about yourself or judge yourself when this happens, even though at times you will.

And don't pretend not to care either. That is just a way to escape the fear or hopelessness of not knowing what to do or how to change.

Feeling however you feel for now, begin with noticing your own actions—the ones that harm you. Trace them back within you to any harmful thoughts you have about yourself or to the feelings that drive them. This is where you need to begin in order to recognise and also heal the pain within you that drives the harm you do. Catching it there within you, as a feeling of distress or pain or numbness or not caring, begins the healing of that particular trauma or pain.

Then you can progress to seeing that all your harmful words or actions begin within you, and that they are connected to any harmful feelings, words or actions that come out of you that have disturbing or harmful effects on others.

Any concern or distress that you feel about this is helpful, even essential, if you can feel it. You can use the concern you have or may even feel about the effects you have on others.

The urge to stop hurting others or stop sabotaging your own life will eventually activate within you. This will happen through you being aware of the effect you have on others and feeling any concern or distress that arises in you over this effect.

It is ultimately *this distress* that will warn you of what you are doing, and also begin to prevent you from continuing any harmful behaviours in your life.

UNDERSTANDING THE ORIGINS OF OUR HARM

Our reactionary and harmful thinking is driven by our unresolved pain from life, our fear of life and also our fear of death.

In reaction to the hard facts of life, we invent alternatives to reality. One example, which occurs mostly due to our fear of death, is when we invent a second self that transcends death. Belief in a second mental or spiritual self is very soothing and numbing to our fears, and very alluring and appealing to our ego. It soothes and numbs us to the harder facts of life, including our mortality.

And of course, soothing is what most of us long for, particularly when we are faced with the death of others or ourself. Our belief in a second self to our mortal body, in an imagined self that may not die when the body dies, provides a partial escape from our fear of death. It's an escape from our fear of reality.

This imagined escape overpowers our rationality. It partially disconnects us from the gravity, significance and appreciation of an individual life, of the finality of life, and from fully living our life now. Therefore, it numbs us and makes it easier for us to do harm by taking a life or by sacrificing our own, or by acting out some mentally disconnected or fanatical idealism.

Ideas and beliefs may provide a way for us to escape our fear of death and pain of loss, but only until we are faced with these factual realities in our own life and begin to feel something again. Then, due to our previous denial of what is reality and when our protective beliefs shatter, the truth can hit us even harder.

Pretending that whomever we lose to death will still live on elsewhere, or pretending that we will, is an avoidance of the only knowable facts, those of our mortality. And that avoidance only prevents us from feeling our loss and healing our grief. Therefore, this belief is harmful to us.

Our belief that we are a spiritual or mental being—additional to the natural creature that we all actually know ourselves to be—is the result of centuries of religion-based indoctrinations. These indoctrinations diminish our sense of and value for the unique individual we are now.

These superstitions also feed our delusions of grandeur that we are 'spiritually superior,' a type of immortal and therefore more important species than other animals. This imagined belief in our superiority has made us harmful to other species. Then over the centuries we have become more creative with this belief and expanded on it to include various levels of importance and hierarchal tyranny, even amongst our own species. This demonstrates that there is no end to such harmful ideas, nor anyway to restrict them to one area of life or to one species. Feeling superior, we simply feel entitled to dominate and feel justified in doing harm.

Why have we come to think like this?

Why do we make up such nonsense?

To escape our own pain or sense of inadequacy, we imagine ourselves superior to anything or anyone, and an unfeeling, separative insanity then emerges. This develops into psychopathic, sociopathic disconnectedness and tyrannical behaviours, which expand endlessly and feed upon themselves.

From the position of any animal that we dominate or terrorise, it is easy to see how we enact these mental illnesses or disconnected behaviours, and that we only act out of this superiority when we are without feelings and empathy.

Ultimately, such ideas and belief in our mental or spiritual superiority are leading to the complete destruction of our natural world, and therefore to our own self-destruction.

ENDING OUR CAPACITY FOR HARM

Ideas, ideals and ideologies are not the answer to ending the harm because they are the products of thought, and so are disconnected, unfeeling and therefore empty of life. Spiritual ideals of being virtuous in our behaviour, of compassion or caring and so on, have to be enforced or intentionally and repeatedly practiced because we don't *feel* ideas, and so they don't naturally impel us.

Ideas are without feeling, which is the physical sensation that we feel and that we are dependent on to naturally drive all our actions. As these ideals are disconnected from the live feeling body of nature that we are, they have little or no impact on their own and so we struggle to live up to them. We have to remember to force ourselves to act on them. Our contradictory feelings will always overpower any mere ideas we have about the way we would like to act.

Ideals and virtues are only needed because of our failure to naturally be able to be this way. But this failure to be guided by our natural kindness and empathy is only possible because of our unfeeling disconnection from the live feeling body of nature that we all are. These ideals have failed us and will continue to fail for those who try to force themselves into being this way.

And by trying to force yourself, you are actually condemning your behaviour and what you are, so you are harming yourself and so already failing. When you fail, you then criticise yourself for failing, and so in criticism of yourself, you will harm yourself yet again. This is why a thought-based approach is not the solution, but is in fact causing you more harm.

The only sure solution is the natural solution, which is to end any separation between parts of your whole self, including the separation of yourself into two, as a body and an imagined mind or spirit self, or a bad self and a good and virtuous self. Dropping this imagined separation re-establishes your reconnection into all of what you are as a natural being, and re-sensitises you. When your thoughts and actions are grounded in your physical feelings and sensations, you will discover that the feelings within yourself and that you have for others and the natural world will prevent you from doing harm. You will then find that it disturbs you more to do harm than it does to go without whatever it was or is that you were trying to get for yourself, by taking forcefully from others, or the world you live in.

When it disturbs you more to do something harmful than it does to not take what you think you want from doing that, or to not impose your ideas or pain on others, there is no thought of or need for virtue. Your own natural state and wholeness of self can't do the harm without you feeling its harmful effects within you. And it is this that will ultimately prevent further harmful behaviours.

In this way, the sensorily interconnected and natural intelligence of the body solves the problem of harmful behaviours that society's enforcement of virtuous behaviours has completely failed to solve. In an automatic way, you are made whole and sensitised and so unable to harm yourself or others or the natural world without feeling great disturbance. And you will find, that as you continue to live with the sensitivity of your whole self, and include all the feelings within you that drive you in life, you will discover a fulfilment in yourself and your life that you will rarely, if ever, have felt before.

SATISFYING THE URGE TO BE AND WANT MORE

When you are disconnected into thinking, that is, into this idea of yourself as a mind separate to the body, because you are desensitised and distracted from reality by this imaginative thinking, you feel empty and incomplete. You feel numbed to and unaware of your effects on others and disconnected from the world, so you try to get more or be more, selfishly disregarding any loss to others. When you live desensitised, you are unaware of others and the world beyond just you and your desires, and so you feel the need to get something out of everything around you or outside of you.

This is why our disconnected and desensitised species has tried to get something out of everything it touches, has drained and abused one another, and has consumed and destroyed the natural environment in which we live. Our sensitivity is our only true intelligence and empathy for life. This is why our attempt to survive by relying on our disconnected, academic intelligence alone hasn't worked, and in fact has turned out to be mostly harmful, even though our intention is to make life better.

In these ways, the disconnected state of our species has been and still is responsible for us feeling empty and unsatisfied in ourselves and unfulfilled by life. This emptiness leads to our perpetual urge for wanting something more for ourselves out of others and out of the world in which we live. This endless wanting to be better and have more comes about because when we are desensitised from our physical selves, we are numb, cold and empty inside. We are also sensorily switched off from and to the living world outside our skin, which is the primary reason we feel unfulfilled.

It is primarily through our sensory connection that we receive and fulfil ourselves with the live abundant energy and direct experience of the world in which we live. It is our senses that connect us and make us receptive to the natural world. And so it is only this sensory connection that provides the experience of being fully connected—a part of and sustained and fulfilled by the world we live in.

This is not mystical at all, but entirely practical, explorable and knowable to every one of us equally, in the following common ways. We all know what it feels like when we are hurt and switched off or withdrawn from another, and how we are then unable to reach out from within that withdrawn or disconnected state to receive or feel support. Only by feeling our hurt and vulnerably reconnecting with another, do we begin to feel relief from their connection and support. That you are unable to be reached in that disconnection is also known to the person trying to reach and care for you. And we know that relief from this disconnection is only possible when we openly reconnect with our pain or with the person from whom we have switched off.

On another level, when we eat food, if we eat slowly and quietly and feel the experience of eating, our digestion works better and so we enhance the effectiveness and absorption of the nutrients and energy for sustaining our life. In fact, whatever we quietly sense, we fully engage with and so fully experience our whole selves at once. Then we're at one with and engaged with life, and so feel an energised and recuperating fulfilment. But we don't even notice this energy of life existing and available to us when we are disconnected or busily thinking.

Again, this is nothing mystical. It's the purely physical, tangible results of being sensorily aware. Because it's nothing mystical, you can explore this purely sensory connection for yourself. Just experiment with any of the above-mentioned situations whenever they are relevant in your life, or right now, by quietly sensing without thinking about what you are sensing. And you will see how fulfilling it is already to just sense your immediate living experience and nothing more. Then you will discover for yourself a sensory connection with the world that fulfils you, without you thinking about what you can get from whatever you are sensorily aware of. And this connection will build on itself within you, whilst taking nothing from the world and others at all.

BEING KIND TO YOURSELF

At first, due to unresolved pain and especially deeper hidden traumas, you will find it difficult to sense or notice the way you feel and so where you are coming from, or to even recognise when these behaviours are coming out of you. Then even when you do, you may not understand why this has happened, or when others point out your behaviours that hurt or distress them, you may not really understand why they feel that way. As you progress with this, you will begin to have more empathy for or at least more patience with yourself.

Deeper pain or hidden trauma, which is held and only known in the way it feels to be you, shows up in your tone of voice or in cutting remarks, in sarcasms or in more obvious anger or rage that just comes out of you at times, with or without you meaning for it to. This is a sign that you are disconnected from what is held deeper within you.

It can be very confusing, and you can feel unfairly criticised when others complain about you. Or you may know that you do this and yet you can't seem to stop yourself from being this way. And you can hate yourself for being this way, which is very distressing and harmful to you.

Although it is important to be kind towards yourself and patient with yourself, this can be difficult because you don't really understand the significance of your pain and what it takes to heal from the deeper, harmful effects of life. Because you don't remember or feel the fullness of that underlying pain, you cannot appreciate how hurt you are inside. This is due to our protective survival mechanism of using thinking to suppress, deny or ignore what happens to us in life. This is a protective or survival reaction to what we find overwhelming, from childhood through to now.

I have consistently found that people who have suffered and suppressed traumas in life have this disconnection from their experience at the time they were hurt. This disconnection can make you blasé or indifferent to your pain or to your past hard times in life. This is because it disables you from truly knowing and feeling the full impact of the hurt and harm you suffered in forgotten or vague past events throughout your life.

Only as you heal more will you find yourself more able to open up to what you still need to feel and so heal from any event you have been through. And you will have more understanding that healing can only happen naturally in its own time, and not by force.

The slower you take it, the faster it takes you. Meaning, the less you push it, fight it, resist it or try to make it happen, and the more you can just go with the process as it unfolds, the more painlessly it will unfold and heal you from within. And as you heal more, you will also learn experientially from your own process that you can feel your felt memory of pain without reacting so much, as the feelings of it purges and heals from within you.

HOW TO STOP HARMING YOURSELF AND OTHERS

A common contradiction of people's lives and of societies as a whole is that while so much emphasis and energy goes into recovering our health and repairing damage in our life, virtually no emphasis or attention goes into eradicating the massively harmful effects of living the way we do and causing all the harm in the first place.

This is because our lost sensory intelligence must be recovered before we can eradicate the cause of harm. We would have to face up to ourselves and evolve out of this disconnected, unintelligent state, and return to being naturally humane. Right there in that, is our solution.

As we are the only species that lives in the violent way we do. We are also the only species that requires healers and the massive framework we have built around patching up the harm we all do to ourselves and others.

In fact, this is the only reason I have felt the need to find new ways to help others heal. Although I have become very good at it, I am also inherently aware of how wrong it is. It shouldn't be necessary. You shouldn't be harmed or harming yourself or others in the first place. I actually consider that healing others is quite unnatural and should not be needed. But it is. But only because of the harm our species do to themselves and to one another.

The unnatural need for healers has occurred purely because of our disconnection from our sensory intelligence and from the consequent harm we are then capable of. This leads to unnatural demand for help with excessive injury, sickness, pain, trauma and insanity that only our species requires help with.

Otherwise, apart from natural injuries from living, harm does not occur in the natural world—for the wild and natural animal. And recovery from such natural injuries is easy.

So which species is the more intelligent?

And what is our measure of intelligence?

The truth of this question of comparing our so-called intelligence with that of animals is difficult to fathom until you begin to recover your body's own natural intelligence and experience its vast superiority over thinking for yourself.

The exclusive focus we have on recovery and repair is the result of our shallow understanding of health and the human condition. It is short sighted, ineffective and unsustainable. It overlooks and excuses the individual for continually harming themselves, which encourages a reckless irresponsibility towards oneself. This path is ultimately harmful to us all.

The alternative approach for sustainable, optimal well-being, simply requires that we recognise and understand the driving source of harm within us, and then learn how to process that to end self-harm. This approach will empower us towards self-reliance and sustainable health and is itself the maturity that is required to address and end harm and end unnecessary suffering for us all.

Which approach would you prefer? Remaining harmful and continually patching up the harm, or ending the potential for more harm?

By feeling and processing your pain, you will go deeper into healing, and you will heal your disconnection and evolve beyond being harmful at all.

Even though this is our ultimate solution, perhaps the only solution, it is however far more challenging to the individual and society to admit and cease that which does us harm, than to continue being harmful and just patching up the damage we cause.

You've taken in a lot of information in this book and now you'll have the opportunity to explore and experiment with this new approach for yourself in your day-to-day actions and interactions.

Go to the Active Meditations for this chapter in the Undo app.

PONDER YOUR PROGRESS

Have you noticed a difference in the frequency and strength of negative or harmful thoughts that you have about yourself or others?

Are you more aware of the many subtle ways we all do harm to each other and are you more able to stop it?

Have you noticed an increased aversion to harming others in any way or a greater disturbance when you do?

Feel free to note any changes that you can see in yourself... subtle changes are often the deepest changes. The deepest changes are often unknown to us at the time of change and are instead only known to us as the improvements in our physical condition and the reduction of our disturbances with real life situations. So take some time out to ponder that.

NOTES:

CONCLUSION

S O NOW YOU HAVE AN ULTIMATE, core solution to all of the problems in life. Whenever you can't do what is good for you and want to give up, before you do, feel the feeling, the sensation inside you that is ruling you. Just hold it right there within you and in this way, let it burn itself out of your system, and it will. Just don't act on it straight away. What you will feel at these times is your most important meditation, and this will always take you into the deepest understanding of yourself, and into resolution.

It has been epic for me to create this transformative information for you. It has pushed me beneficially in ways that I didn't anticipate before I began writing the app but it is also deeply fulfilling for me to be able to share this with you. The totality of the information presented in the Undo app itself is designed with many profound and deep layers.

As you have progressed through this introduction to natural meditation, you will have learned a lot about the way you—the body—functions. As your experiential depth in your own understanding has grown, you will have developed and changed along the way. And because of this, I suggest you take your time to repeat any section that appealed to you or that you may have bookmarked. Alternatively you can download the app and work through all of it to experience the full effect, if you haven't done that already.

Consider revisiting any section that didn't appeal to you or that you found especially challenging or perhaps even skipped. You may feel quite differently about that information now. Or you could simply start from the beginning and read it all over again. This way you'll see for yourself how much your understanding has grown, how much you have grown and changed, and how much you can now benefit from whatever you may have misunderstood or missed the first time around.

After all the changes that have happened in you, and the massive expansion that will have occurred in your understanding of yourself, you'll be able to glean much more from each chapter, and so be able to see and receive much, much more.

You'll discover differences in yourself that you may not have realised, and be encouraged by the inevitable changes that will have happened—both the obvious and the many subtle ones. This will help you recognise and appreciate a renewed and recovered you that is closer to your original and natural state than it was before.

Also, because many of the significant changes within you will have occurred on a deeper level than what you are used to, they may not be so obvious at first. Where you will notice the more impactful changes is in how you feel, how you now think about yourself, in your improved physical health, and in the many small ways you cope better in life and in your relationships and with others. So, give yourself time to discover and appreciate these deeper changes. The simplest way to do that is to work your way through the meditations within the app.

By learning how to look after your mental and physical health you can save tons on medical costs and therapy. Just look at the total on your hidden-stress cost list. Now that you have read this book, you'll now know that healing and recovering from the daily stresses of life and the past are possible, through simply feeling your feelings and not avoiding them.

You can learn a lot from this book and from using the app and if it has resonated with you, there is also the option to work with me personally. Working with me one-on-one would naturally enable you to go deeper and therefore learn a lot more, and more quickly, than the self-guided approach.

Welcome to a new chapter in your life. I hope you got as much out of reading this book as I did from creating it.

READER RESOURCES

CHECKLIST FOR WHEN YOU'RE STUCK

Wow well done! You've really achieved a lot in reading this far. We hope you've enjoyed the journey and that your new approach to yourself and your life has opened up a whole new world for you.

Here are a few tips and reminders to help support you in living your new understanding both now and for the rest of your life.

If ever you struggle with implementing any part of the Undo approach in your life, always check whether the following first step is covered. This will expose and remove the barrier causing your struggle, and ground you into your ultimate solution of being anchored again in the true and physical sense of yourself.

THE FIRST STEP

- The only problem you will have with successfully implementing the Undo approach into your life will come out of all the obvious and subtle ways you try to avoid feeling your pain or distress.
- The solution, every time, relies on you admitting to your distractions and attempts to fix your pain or to blame others or the world for it. Then by coming back to the felt sensations in your body, to reconnect with the feelings of any pain or distress, wherever you feel it in your body.
- And do absolutely nothing more than this.
- Remember, trying to fix your pain is a reaction and avoidance, and trying to change yourself is as well. So the only solution is for you to stay with yourself however you feel or are, and give your body and entire system time to resolve itself naturally, and it will.

BEWARE OF

- Acting on your urge to avoid pain or project blame, or to believe your pain is the fault of others. This will not help you, it will harm you more. By you feeling the pain or urge to lash out or harm others at its source, it will dissipate and you'll heal that urge and end it there, harmlessly within you. That is ultimately the only way to save you and others from further harm.

- Remember, old harm or pain is there to heal you, not harm you more, and as long as you are feeling it without mentally reacting to it, it will be a relief to feel it not a suffering. And the benefit is that you will evolve and deepen through approaching your pain in this way.

DON'T AVOID YOUR PAIN OR MEDITATION

- Whenever you stray from yourself by avoiding your pain or your meditation, you are acting on your one and *only* difficulty—that of avoiding how it feels to be you deeper inside you. And whatever you avoid remains hidden within and causes all other difficulties.
- Your one and only difficulty will always come back to this—you won't want to feel the pain within you, or live with and feel your destructive urges to their end, without seeking a temporary relief by acting on them. *Not* giving into and acting on your pain driven or harmful urges will be your only struggle and potential point of failure, which ultimately is, giving up on yourself.
- Don't weaken yourself or complicate this or your life by thinking about or seeking easier solutions. Know now that there aren't any.
- Not avoiding your inner self or acting on harmful urges is your only solution. What that exposes is that the way you feel behind these urges is the driving force responsible for any harmful or habitual behaviours. That feeling is your most important meditation, right then and there. That is

all that is required of you to change whatever it is that's causing the harm, and end the harm from within you. It's as simple as that, and that's all there is to it. I'm not saying it is easy to stay with your pain, but, this one solution is truly that simple. So don't complicate it by overthinking or avoiding yourself.

A BETTER WAY

The only way your pain can continue to harm you or others or cause further destruction in your life is if you give into the urge and act it out through thoughts, words or actions. So don't. Now you have a better way, and one that actually works. Just keep it where it is, hold it within you until it eventually calms down, dissipates and heals inside you. And in this way, end all harm there, within you.

STICK TO THE BASICS

These are some simple ways in which you can begin to stop harming yourself. They are essential for you to sustain rather than inhibit your own continual healing or development. It will also help you, if as a general practice, you don't overlook the very basic things. Put off eating the junk food, smoking or drinking toxic drinks like alcohol.

But of all things, the most toxic to your body is harmful thinking. So most importantly, stop criticising yourself or others and refuse any socially acceptable forms of self-harm. Whatever your current demon is—taking drugs, escaping into music, obsessively checking your phone, pushing yourself when you're already tired, not thinking for yourself, believing what you don't understand, overeating or even excessively snacking—it all comes from pain, and it all continues the harm and pain that you avoid, already within you.

"YOUR WELLBEING DEPENDS
ON YOUR HONESTY"

Hidden-stress cost calculator

List your costs here. Draw up a simple table with three columns —money, energy and time.

ABOUT THE AUTHOR

MATTHEW ZOLTAN currently lives in Europe. He is the co-founder of a number of businesses all revolving around his life work of Natural Meditation. His businesses include Undo and Quiet Retreats. He also has a private clinic which is open to local and international clients online. He speaks publicly to a variety of industries via podcasts and by private engagement. His services also include mentoring and advising on mergers and exits to SME's. If you need assistance or support for yourself or your company, go to mattzoltan.com.

Currently involved in planning an alternative health retreat with his friends, in the near future he will be offering a space for people to recover and detox in a holistic and connected way.

You can download and read his white paper on the undoapp.com website.

He will be offering certification courses and teacher training for natural meditation very soon. To book in for any of his courses and certifications keep an eye on the quietretreats.co website or email his team hello@quietretreats.co.

Matthew holds long, silent residential natural meditation retreats year-round. If you would like to be updated, subscribe to his newsletter on the quietretreats.co website.

If you'd like to interview Matthew on your podcast or have him speak at a public event, go to mattzoltan.com or email the team enquiries@mattzoltan.com.

Matthew doesn't want anyone to miss out on this fundamental information for navigating life. If you are under financial hardship or would like to share this book with your friends please email his team at hey@undoapp.com and request a free version of the app or the book (we do ask that you pay for the shipping of the book).

Use the code UNDOBOOK23 to receive 1 month free on Undo's annual subscription.

Printed in Poland
by Amazon Fulfillment
Poland Sp. z o.o., Wrocław

50570849R00146